85

- 15

Ruth M. Crimmes.

WENTWORTH-SMITH MATHEMATICAL SERIES

PLANE GEOMETRY

BY

GEORGE WENTWORTH

AND

DAVID EUGENE SMITH

GINN AND COMPANY
BOSTON · NEW YORK · CHICAGO · LONDON

The Athenæum Press
GINN AND COMPANY · PRO-
PRIETORS · BOSTON · U.S.A.

PREFACE

Long after the death of Robert Recorde, England's first great writer of textbooks, the preface of a new edition of one of his works contained the appreciative statement that the book was "entail'd upon the People, ratified and sign'd by the approbation of Time." The language of this sentiment sounds quaint, but the noble tribute is as impressive to-day as when first put in print two hundred and fifty years ago.

With equal truth these words may be applied to the Geometry written by George A. Wentworth. For a generation it has been the leading textbook on the subject in America. It set a standard for usability that every subsequent writer upon geometry has tried to follow, and the number of pupils who have testified to its excellence has run well into the millions.

In undertaking to prepare a work to take the place of the Wentworth Geometry the authors have been guided by certain well-defined principles, based upon an extended investigation of the needs of the schools and upon a study of all that is best in the recent literature of the subject. The effects of these principles they feel should be summarized for the purpose of calling the attention of the wide circle of friends of the Wentworth-Smith series to the points of similarity and of difference in the two works.

1. Every effort has been made not only to preserve but to improve upon the simplicity of treatment, the clearness of expression, and the symmetry of page that characterized the successive editions of the Wentworth Geometry. It has been the purpose to prepare a book that should do even more than maintain the traditions this work has fostered.

2. The proofs have been given substantially in full, to the end that the pupil may always have before him a model for his independent treatment of the exercises.

3. The sequence of propositions has been improved in several respects, notably in the treatment of parallels.

4. To meet a general demand, the number of propositions has been decreased so as to include only the great basal theorems and problems. A little of the less important material has been placed in the Appendix, to be used or not as circumstances demand.

5. The exercises, in some respects the most important part of a course in geometry, have been rendered more dignified in appearance and have been improved in content. The number of simple exercises has been greatly increased, while the difficult puzzle is much less in evidence than in most American textbooks. The exercises are systematically grouped, appearing in full pages, in large type, at frequent intervals. They are not all intended for one class, but are so numerous as to allow the teacher to make selections from year to year.

6. The introduction has been made as concrete as is reasonable. Definitions have been postponed until they are actually needed, only well-recognized terms have been employed, the pupil is initiated at once into the practical use of the instruments, some of the reasons for studying geometry are early shown in an interesting way, and correlation is made with the simple algebra already studied.

The authors are indebted to many friends of the Wentworth-Smith series for assistance and encouragement in the labor of preparing this work, and they will welcome any further suggestions for improvement from any of their readers.

GEORGE WENTWORTH
DAVID EUGENE SMITH

CONTENTS

SYMBOLS AND ABBREVIATIONS

= equals, equal, equal to, is equal to, or is equivalent to.

> is greater than.

< is less than.

‖ parallel.

⊥ perpendicular.

∠ angle.

△ triangle.

▱ parallelogram.

▭ rectangle.

⊙ circle.

st. straight.

rt. right.

∵ since.

∴ therefore.

Adj. adjacent.

Alt. alternate.

Ax. axiom.

Const. construction.

Cor. corollary.

Def. definition.

Ex. exercise.

Ext. exterior.

Fig. figure.

Hyp. hypothesis.

Iden. identity.

Int. interior.

Post. postulate.

Prob. problem.

Prop. proposition.

Sup. supplementary.

These symbols take the plural form when necessary, as in the case of ‖s, ∠s, △s, ⊙s.

The symbols $+$, $-$, $\times$, $\div$ are used as in algebra.

There is no generally accepted symbol for "is congruent to," and the words are used in this book. Some teachers use ≅ or ≌, and some use ≡, but the sign of equality is more commonly employed, the context telling whether equality, equivalence, or congruence is to be understood.

Q. E. D. is an abbreviation that has long been used in geometry for the Latin words *quod erat demonstrandum*, "which was to be proved."

Q. E. F. stands for *quod erat faciendum*, "which was to be done."

PLANE GEOMETRY

INTRODUCTION

1. The Nature of Arithmetic. In arithmetic we study computation, the working with numbers. We may have a formula expressed in algebraic symbols, such as $a = bh$, where a may stand for the area of a rectangle, and b and h respectively for the number of units of length in the base and height; but the actual computation involved in applying such formula to a particular case is part of arithmetic.

2. The Nature of Algebra. In algebra we generalize the arithmetic, and instead of saying that the area of a rectangle with base 4 in. and height 2 in. is 4×2 sq. in., we express a general law by saying that $a = bh$. In arithmetic we may have an equality, like $2 \times 16 + 17 = 49$, but in algebra we make much use of equations, like $2x + 17 = 49$. Algebra, therefore, is a generalized arithmetic.

3. The Nature of Geometry. We are now about to begin another branch of mathematics, one not chiefly relating to numbers although it uses numbers, and not primarily devoted to equations although using them, but one that is concerned principally with the study of forms, such as triangles, parallelograms, and circles. Many facts that are stated in arithmetic and algebra are proved in geometry. For example, in geometry it is proved that the square on the hypotenuse of a right triangle equals the sum of the squares on the other two sides, and that the circumference of a circle equals 3.1416 times the diameter.

1

4. Solid. The block here represented is called a *solid;* it is a limited portion of space filled with matter. In geometry, however, we have nothing to do with the matter of which a

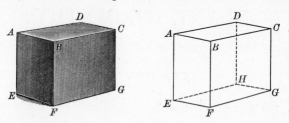

body is composed; we study simply its *shape* and *size*, as in the second figure.

That is, a physical solid can be touched and handled; a geometric solid is the space that a physical solid is conceived to occupy. For example, a stick is a physical solid ; but if we put it into wet plaster, and then remove it, the hole that is left may be thought of as a geometric solid although it is filled with air.

5. Geometric Solid. A limited portion of space is called a *geometric solid.*

6. Dimensions. The block represented in § 4 extends in three principal directions :

　　(1) From left to right, that is, from A to D;

　　(2) From back to front, that is, from A to B;

　　(3) From top to bottom, that is, from A to E.

These extensions are called the *dimensions* of the block, and are named in the order given, *length, breadth* (or width), and *thickness* (height, altitude, or depth). Similarly, we may say that every solid has three dimensions.

Very often a solid is of such shape that we cannot point out the length, or distinguish it from the breadth or thickness, as an irregular block of coal. In the case of a round ball, where the length, breadth, and thickness are all the same in extent, it is impossible to distinguish one dimension from the others.

7. Surface. The block shown in § 4 has six flat faces, each of which is called a *surface*. If the faces are made smooth by polishing, so that when a straight edge is applied to any one of them the straight edge in every part will touch the surface, each face is called a *plane surface*, or a *plane*.

These surfaces are simply the boundaries of the solid. They have no thickness, even as a colored light shining upon a piece of paper does not make the paper thicker. A board may be planed thinner and thinner, and then sandpapered still thinner, thus coming nearer and nearer to representing what we think of as a geometric plane, but it is always a solid bounded by surfaces.

That which has length and breadth without thickness is called a *surface*.

8. Line. In the solid shown in § 4 we see that two adjacent surfaces intersect in a line. A line is therefore simply the boundary of a surface, and has neither breadth nor thickness.

That which has length without breadth or thickness is called a *line*.

A telegraph wire, for example, is not a line. It is a solid. Even a pencil mark has width and a very little thickness, so that it is also a solid. But if we think of a wire as drawn out so that it becomes finer and finer, it comes nearer and nearer to representing what we think of and speak of as a geometric line.

9. Magnitudes. Solids, surfaces, and lines are called *magnitudes*.

10. Point. In the solid shown in § 4 we see that when two lines meet they meet in a point. A point is therefore simply the boundary of a line, and has no length, no breadth, and no thickness.

That which has only position, without length, breadth, or thickness, is called a *point*.

We may think of the extremity of a line as a point. We may also think of the intersection of two lines as a point, and of the intersection of two surfaces as a line.

11. Representing Points and Geometric Magnitudes. Although we only imagine such geometric magnitudes as lines or planes, we may represent them by pictures.

Thus we represent a point by a fine dot, and name it by a letter, as P in this figure.

We represent a line by a fine mark, and name it by letters placed at the ends, as AB.

We represent a surface by its boundary lines, and name it by letters placed at the corners or in some other convenient way, as $ABCD$.

We represent a solid by the boundary faces or by the lines bounding the faces, as in § 4.

12. Generation of Geometric Magnitudes. We may think of

     (1) A line as generated by a moving point;

     (2) A surface as generated by a moving line;

     (3) A solid as generated by a moving surface.

For example, as shown in the figure let the surface $ABCD$ move to the position $WXYZ$. Then

     (1) A generates the line AW;

     (2) AB generates the surface $AWXB$;

     (3) $ABCD$ generates the solid AY.

Of course a point will not generate a line by simply turning over, for this is not motion for a point; nor will a line generate a surface by simply sliding along itself; nor will a surface generate a solid by simply sliding upon itself.

13. Geometric Figure. A point, a line, a surface, a solid, or any combination of these, is called a *geometric figure.*

A geometric figure is generally called simply a *figure.*

14. Geometry. The science of geometric figures is called *geometry.*

Plane geometry treats of figures that lie wholly in the same plane, that is, of plane figures.

Solid geometry treats of figures that do not lie wholly in the same plane.

15. Straight Line. A line such that any part placed with its ends on any other part must lie wholly in the line is called a *straight line.*

For example, AB is a straight line, for if we take, say, a half inch of it, and place it in any way on any other part of AB, but so that its ends lie in AB, then the whole of the half inch of line will lie in AB. This is well shown by using tracing paper. The word *line* used alone is understood to mean a straight line.

Part of a straight line is called a *segment* of the line. The term *segment* is applied also to certain other magnitudes.

16. Equality of Lines. Two straight-line segments that can be placed one upon the other so that their extremities coincide are said to be *equal.*

In general, two geometric magnitudes are equal if they can be made to coincide throughout their whole extent. We shall see later that some figures that coincide are said to be *congruent.*

17. Broken Line. A line made up of two or more different straight lines is called a *broken line.*

For example, CD is a broken line.

18. Rectilinear Figure. A plane figure formed by a broken line is called a *rectilinear figure.*

For example, $ABCD$ is a rectilinear figure.

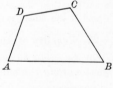

19. Curve Line. A line no part of which is straight is called a *curve line*, or simply a *curve.*

For example, EF is a curve line.

20. Curvilinear Figure. A plane figure formed by a curve line is called a *curvilinear figure.*

For example, O is a curvilinear figure with which we are already familiar.

Some curvilinear figures are surfaces bounded by curves and others are the curves themselves.

21. Angle. The opening between two straight lines drawn from the same point is called an *angle*.

Strictly speaking, this is a *plane* angle. We shall find later that there are angles made by curve lines and angles made by planes.

The two lines are called the *sides* of the angle, and the point of meeting is called the *vertex*.

An angle may be read by naming the letters designating the sides, the vertex letter being between the others, as the angle *A OB*. An angle may also be designated by the vertex letter, as the angle *O*, or by a small letter within, as the angle *m*. A curve is often drawn to show the particular angle meant, as in angle *m*.

22. Size of Angle. The size of an angle depends upon the amount of turning necessary to bring one side into the position of the other.

One angle is greater than another angle when the amount of turning is greater. Thus in these compasses the first angle is smaller than the second, which is also smaller than the third. The length of the sides has nothing to do with the size of the angle.

23. Equality of Angles. Two angles that can be placed one upon the other so that their vertices coincide and the sides of one lie along the sides of the other are said to be *equal*.

For example, the angles *A OB* and *A'O'B'* (read "*A* prime, *O* prime, *B* prime") are equal. It is well to illustrate this by tracing one on thin paper and placing it upon the other.

24. Bisector. A point, a line, or a plane that divides a geometric magnitude into two equal parts is called a *bisector* of the magnitude.

For example, *M*, the mid-point of the line *AB*, is a bisector of the line.

A   *M*   B

25. Adjacent Angles. Two angles that have the same vertex and a common side between them are called *adjacent angles*.

For example, the angles AOB and BOC are adjacent angles, and in § 26 the angles AOB and BOC are adjacent angles.

26. Right Angle. When one straight line meets another straight line and makes the adjacent angles equal, each angle is called a *right angle*.

For example, angles AOB and BOC in this figure. If CO is cut off, angle AOB is still a right angle.

27. Perpendicular. A straight line making a right angle with another straight line is said to be *perpendicular* to it.

Thus OB is perpendicular to CA, and CA to OB. OB is also called *a perpendicular* to CA, and O is called the *foot* of the perpendicular OB.

28. Triangle. A portion of a plane bounded by three straight lines is called a *triangle*.

The lines AB, BC, and CA are called the *sides* of the triangle ABC, and the sides taken together form the *perimeter*. The points A, B, and C are the *vertices* of the triangle, and the angles A, B, and C are the *angles* of the triangle. The side AB upon which the triangle is supposed to rest is the *base* of the triangle. Similarly for other plane figures.

29. Circle. A closed curve lying in a plane, and such that all of its points are equally distant from a fixed point in the plane, is called a *circle*.

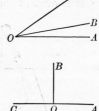

The length of the circle is called the *circumference*. The point from which all points on the circle are equally distant is the *center*. Any portion of a circle is an *arc*. A straight line from the center to the circle is a *radius*. A straight line through the center, terminated at each end by the circle, is a *diameter*.

Formerly in elementary geometry *circle* was taken to mean the space inclosed, and the bounding line was called the circumference. Modern usage has conformed to the definition used in higher mathematics.

30. Instruments of Geometry. In geometry only two instruments are necessary besides pencil and paper. These are a straight edge, or ruler, and a pair of compasses.

It is evident that *all radii of the same circle are equal.*

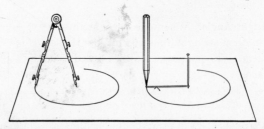

In the absence of compasses, and particularly for blackboard work, a loop made of string may be used. For the accurate transfer of lengths, however, compasses are desirable.

31. Exercises in using Instruments. The following simple exercises are designed to accustom the pupil to the use of instruments. No proofs are attempted, these coming later in the course.

This section may be omitted if desired, without affecting the course.

EXERCISE 1

1. From a given point on a given straight line required to draw a perpendicular to the line.

Let AB be the given line and P be the given point.

It is required to draw from P a line perpendicular to AB.

With P as a center and any convenient radius draw arcs cutting AB at X and Y.

With X as a center and XY as a radius draw a circle, and with Y as a center and the same radius draw another circle, and call one intersection of the circles C.

With a straight edge draw a line from P to C, and this will be the perpendicular required.

2. From a given point outside a given straight line required to let fall a perpendicular to the line.

Let AB be the given straight line and P be the given point.

It is required to draw from P a line perpendicular to AB.

With P as a center and any convenient radius draw an arc cutting AB at X and Y.

With X as a center and any convenient radius draw a circle, and with Y as a center and the same radius draw another circle, and call one intersection of the circles C.

With a straight edge draw a straight line from P to C, and this will be the perpendicular required.

It is interesting to test the results in Exs. 1 and 2, by cutting the paper and fitting the angles together.

3. Required to draw a triangle having two sides each equal to a given line.

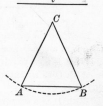

Let l be the given line.

It is required to draw a triangle having two sides each equal to l.

With any center, as C, and a radius equal to l draw an arc.

Join any two points on the arc, as A and B, with each other and with C by straight lines.

Then ABC is the triangle required.

4. Required to draw a triangle having its three sides each equal to a given line.

Let AB be the given line.

It is required to draw a triangle having its three sides each equal to AB.

With A as a center and AB as a radius draw a circle, and with B as a center and the same radius draw another circle.

Join either intersection of the circles with A and B by straight lines.

Then ABC is the triangle required.

In such cases draw the arcs only long enough to show the point of intersection.

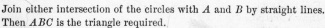

5. Required to draw a triangle having its sides equal respectively to three given lines.

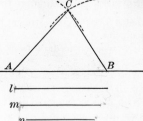

Let the three lines be *l*, *m*, and *n*.

What is now required?

Upon any line mark off with the compasses a line-segment *AB* equal to *l*.

With *A* as a center and *m* as a radius draw a circle; with *B* as a center and *n* as a radius draw a circle.

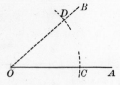

Draw *AC* and *BC*.

Then *ABC* is the required triangle.

6. From a given point on a given line required to draw a line making an angle equal to a given angle.

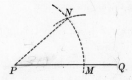

Let *P* be the given point on the given line *PQ*, and let angle *AOB* be the given angle.

What is now required?

With *O* as a center and any radius draw an arc cutting *AO* at *C* and *BO* at *D*.

With *P* as a center and *OC* as a radius draw an arc cutting *PQ* at *M*.

With *M* as a center and the straight line joining *C* and *D* as a radius draw an arc cutting the arc just drawn at *N*, and draw *PN*.

Then angle *MPN* is the required angle.

7. Required to bisect a given straight line.

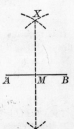

Let *AB* be the given line.

It is required to bisect *AB*.

With *A* as a center and *AB* as a radius draw a circle, and with *B* as a center and the same radius draw a circle.

Call the two intersections of the circles *X* and *Y*.

Draw the straight line *XY*.

Then *XY* bisects the line *AB* at the point of intersection *M*.

8. Required to bisect a given angle.

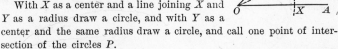

Let AOB be the given angle.

It is required to bisect the angle AOB.

With O as a center and any convenient radius draw an arc cutting OA at X and OB at Y.

With X as a center and a line joining X and Y as a radius draw a circle, and with Y as a center and the same radius draw a circle, and call one point of intersection of the circles P.

Draw the straight line OP.

Then OP is the required bisector.

9. By the use of compasses and ruler draw the following figures:

The dotted lines show how to fix the points needed in drawing the figure, and they may be erased after the figure is completed. In general, in geometry, auxiliary lines (those needed only as aids) are indicated by dotted lines.

10. By the use of compasses and ruler draw the following figures:

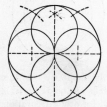 

It is apparent from the figures in Exs. 9 and 10 that the radius of the circle may be used in describing arcs that shall divide the circle into six equal parts.

11. By the use of compasses and ruler draw the following figures :

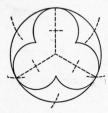 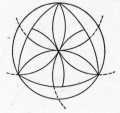

12. By the use of compasses and ruler draw the following figures :

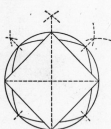 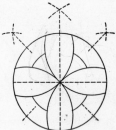

13. By the use of compasses and ruler draw the following figures :

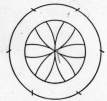 

In such figures artistic patterns may be made by coloring various portions of the drawings. In this way designs are made for stained-glass windows, for oilcloth, for colored tiles, and for other decorations.

14. Draw a triangle of which each side is $1\frac{1}{4}$ in.

15. Draw two lines bisecting each other at right angles.

16. Bisect each of the four right angles formed by two lines bisecting each other at right angles.

17. Draw a line $1\frac{1}{2}$ in. long and divide it into eighths of an inch, using the ruler. Then with the compasses draw this figure.

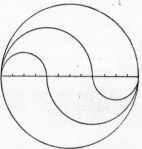

It is easily shown, when we come to the measurement of the circle, that these two curve lines divide the space inclosed by the circle into parts that are exactly equal to one another.

By continuing each semicircle to make a complete circle another interesting figure is formed. Other similar designs are easily invented, and students should be encouraged to make such original designs.

18. In planning a Gothic window this drawing is needed. The arc BC is drawn with A as a center and AB as a radius. The small arches are described with A, D, and B as centers and AD as a radius. The center P is found by taking A and B as centers and AE as a radius. How may the points D, E, and F be found? Draw the figure.

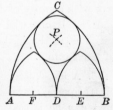

19. Draw a triangle of which each side is 1 in. Bisect each side, and with the points of bisection as centers and with radii $\frac{1}{2}$ in. long draw three circles.

20. A baseball diamond is a square 90 ft. on a side. Draw the plan, using a scale of $\frac{1}{16}$ in. to a foot. Locate the pitcher 60 ft. from the home plate.

21. A man travels from A directly east 1 mi. to B. He then turns and travels directly north $1\frac{3}{4}$ mi. to C. Draw the plan and find by measurement the distance AC to the nearest quarter of a mile. Use a scale of $\frac{1}{2}$ in. to a mile.

22. A double tennis court is 78 ft. long and 36 ft. wide. The net is placed 39 ft. from each end and the service lines 18 ft. from each end. Draw the plan, using a scale of $\frac{1}{16}$ in. to a foot, making the right angles as shown in Ex. 1. The accuracy of the construction may be tested by measuring the diagonals, which should be equal.

23. At the entrance to New York harbor is a gun having a range of 12 mi. Draw a line inclosing the range of fire, using a scale of $\frac{1}{16}$ in. to a mile.

24. Two forts are placed on opposite sides of a harbor entrance, 13 mi. apart. Each has a gun having a range of 10 mi. Draw a plan showing the area exposed to the fire of both guns, using a scale of $\frac{1}{16}$ in. to a mile.

25. Two forts, A and B, are placed on opposite sides of a harbor entrance, 16 mi. apart. On an island in the harbor, 12 mi. from A and 11 mi. from B, is a fort C. The fort A has a gun with a range of 12 mi., fort B one with a range of 11 mi., and fort C one with a range of 10 mi. Draw a plan of the entrance to the harbor, showing the area exposed to the fire of each gun.

26. A horse, tied by a rope 25 ft. long at the corner of a lot 50 ft. square, grazes over as much of the lot as possible. The next day he is tied at the next corner, the third day at the third corner, and the fourth day at the fourth corner. Draw a plan showing the area over which he has grazed during the four days, using a scale of $\frac{1}{8}$ in. to 5 ft.

27. A gardener laid out a flower bed on the following plan : He made a triangle ABC, 16 ft. on a side, and then bisected two of the angles. From the point of intersection of the bisectors, P, he drew perpendiculars to the three sides of the triangle, PX, PY, and PZ. Then he drew a circle with P as a center and PX as a radius, and found that it just fitted in the triangle. Draw the plan, using a scale of $\frac{1}{4}$ in. to a foot.

32. Necessity for Proof. Although part of geometry consists in drawing figures, this is not the most important part. It is essential to prove that the figures are what we claim them to be. The danger of trusting to appearances is seen in Exercise 2.

EXERCISE 2

1. Estimate which is the longer line, *AB* or *XY*, and how much longer. Then test your estimate by measuring with the compasses or with a piece of paper carefully marked.

2. Estimate which is the longer line, *AB* or *CD*, and how much longer. Then test your estimate by measuring as in Ex. 1.

3. Look at this figure and state whether *AB* and *CD* are both straight lines. If one is not straight, which one is it? Test your answer by using a ruler or the folded edge of a piece of paper.

4. Look at this figure and state whether *AB* and *CD* are the same distance apart at *A* and *C* as at *B* and *D*. Then test your answer as in Ex. 1.

5. Look at this figure and state whether *AB* will, if prolonged, lie on *CD*. Also state whether *WX* will, if prolonged, lie on *YZ*. Then test your answer by laying a ruler along the lines.

6. Look at this figure and state which of the three lower lines is *AB* prolonged. Then test your answer by laying a ruler along *AB*.

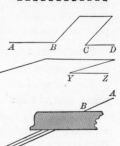

33. Straight Angle. When the sides of an angle extend in opposite directions, so as to be in the same straight line, the angle is called a *straight angle.*

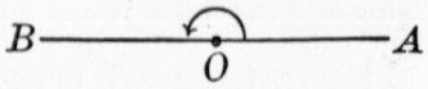

B———⌒———A
   O

For example, the angle *AOB*, as shown in this figure, is a straight angle. The angle *BOA*, below the line, is also a straight angle.

34. Right Angle and Straight Angle. It follows from the definition of right angle (§ 26) that *a right angle is half of a straight angle.*

In like manner, it follows that *a straight angle equals twice a right angle.*

35. Acute Angle. An angle less than a right angle is called an *acute angle.*

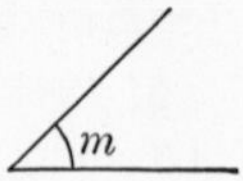

For example, the angle *m*, as shown in this figure, is an acute angle.

36. Obtuse Angle. An angle greater than a right angle and less than a straight angle is called an *obtuse angle.*

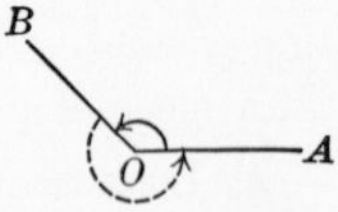

For example, the angle *AOB*, as shown in this figure, is an obtuse angle.

37. Reflex Angle. An angle greater than a straight angle and less than two straight angles is called a *reflex angle.*

For example, the angle *BOA*, marked with a dotted curve line in the figure in § 36, is a reflex angle.

When we speak of an angle formed by two given lines drawn from a point we mean the smaller angle unless the contrary is stated.

38. Oblique Angles. Acute angles and obtuse angles are called *oblique angles.*

The sides of oblique angles are said to be *oblique* to each other, and are called *oblique lines.*

Evidently if we bisect a straight angle, we form two right angles; if we bisect a right angle or an obtuse angle, we form two acute angles; if we bisect a reflex angle, we form two obtuse angles.

39. Generation of Angles. Suppose the line r to revolve from the position OA about the point O as a vertex to the position OB. Then r describes or generates the *acute angle AOB*, and, as we have seen (§ 22) *the size of the angle depends upon the amount of rotation*, the angle being greater as the amount of turning is greater.

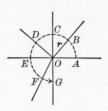

If r rotates still further, to the position OC, it has then generated the *right angle AOC* and is perpendicular to OA.

If r rotates still further, to the position OD, it has then generated the *obtuse angle AOD*.

If r rotates to the position OE, it has then generated the *straight angle AOE*.

If r rotates to the position OF, it has then generated the *reflex angle AOF*.

If r rotates still further, past OG to the position OA again, it has made a complete revolution and has generated two straight angles or four right angles.

40. Sums and Differences of Magnitudes. If the straight line AP has been generated by a point P moving from A to P, the segments AB, BC, CD, and so on, having been generated in succession, then we call AC the *sum* of AB and BC. That is,

$$AC = AB + BC, \text{ whence } AC - BC = AB.$$

If the angle AOD has been generated by the line OA revolving about O as a vertex from the position OA, the angles AOB, BOC, and COD having been generated in succession, then we call angle AOC the *sum* of angles AOB and BOC. That is, considering angles,

$$AOC = AOB + BOC, \text{ whence } AOC - BOC = AOB.$$

In the same way that we may have the sum or the difference of lines or of angles we may have the sum or the difference of surfaces or of solids.

41. Perigon. The whole angular space in a plane about a point is called a *perigon*.

It therefore follows that a perigon equals the sum of two straight angles or the sum of four right angles.

42. Complements, Supplements, and Conjugates. If the sum of two angles is a right angle, each angle is called the *complement* of the other.

If the sum of two angles is a straight angle, each angle is called the *supplement* of the other.

If the sum of two angles is a perigon, each angle is called the *conjugate* of the other.

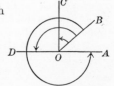

Thus, with respect to angle AOB,
     the *complement* is angle BOC,
     the *supplement* is angle BOD,
     the *conjugate* is angle BOA (reflex).

43. Properties of Supplementary Angles. It is sufficiently evident to be taken without proof that

1. *The two adjacent angles which one straight line makes with another are together equal to a straight angle.*

2. *If the sum of two adjacent angles is a straight angle, their exterior sides are in the same straight line.*

44. Angle Measure. Angles are measured by taking as a unit $\frac{1}{360}$ of a perigon. This unit is called a *degree*.

The degree is divided into 60 equal parts, called *minutes*, and the minute into 60 equal parts, called *seconds*.

We write 5° 13′ 12″ for 5 degrees 13 minutes 12 seconds.

It is evident that a right angle equals 90°, a straight angle equals 180°, and a perigon equals 360°.

45. Vertical Angles. When two angles have the same vertex, and the sides of the one are prolongations of the sides of the other, those angles are called *vertical angles.*

In the figure the angles x and z are vertical angles, as are also the angles w and y.

EXERCISE 3

1. Find the complement of $72°$; of $65° 30'$; of $22° 20' 15''$.

2. What is the supplement of $45°$? of $120°$? of $145° 5'$? of $22° 20' 15''$?

3. What is the conjugate of $240°$? of $280°$? of $312° 10' 40''$?

4. The complement of a certain angle x is $2x$. How many degrees are there in x?

5. The complement of a certain angle x is $3x$. How many degrees are there in x?

6. What is the angle of which the complement is four times the angle itself?

7. The supplement of a certain angle x is $5x$. How many degrees are there in x?

8. The supplement of a certain angle x is $14x$. How many degrees are there in x?

9. What is the angle of which the supplement equals half of the angle itself?

10. How many degrees in an angle that equals its own complement? in one that equals its own supplement?

11. The conjugate of a certain angle x is $\frac{2}{3}x$. How many degrees are there in x?

12. The conjugate of a certain angle x is $\frac{1}{2}x$. How many degrees are there in x?

13. How many degrees in an angle that equals a third of its own conjugate? in one that equals its own conjugate?

14. Find two angles, x and y, such that their sum is $90°$ and their difference is $10°$.

15. Find two complementary angles such that their difference is $30°$.

16. Find two supplementary angles such that one is $20°$ greater than the other.

17. The angles x and y are conjugate angles, and their difference is a straight angle. How many degrees are there in each?

18. The angles x and y are conjugate angles, and their difference is zero. How many degrees are there in each?

19. Of two complementary angles one is four fifths of the other. How many degrees are there in each?

20. Of two supplementary angles one is five times the other. How many degrees are there in each?

21. How many degrees are there in the smaller angle formed by the hands of a clock at 5 o'clock?

22. How many degrees are there in the smaller angle formed by the hands of a clock at 10 o'clock?

23. In this figure, if angle AOB is 38°, how many degrees in angle BOC? How many in angle COD? How many in angle DOA?

24. In the same figure, if angle AOB is equal to a third of angle BOC, how many degrees in each of the four angles?

25. In the angles of this figure, if $w = 2x$, how many degrees in each? How many degrees in y? How many degrees in z?

26. Find the angle whose complement decreased by 30° equals the angle itself.

27. Find the angle whose complement divided by 2 equals the angle itself.

28. Draw a figure to show that if two adjacent angles have their exterior sides in the same straight line, their sum is a straight angle.

29. Draw a figure to show that the sum of all the angles on the same side of a straight line, at a given point, is equal to two right angles.

30. Draw a figure to show that the complements of equal angles are equal.

46. Axiom. A general statement admitted without proof to be true is called an *axiom*.

For example, it is stated in algebra that "if equals are added to equals the sums are equal." This is so simple that it is generally accepted without proof. It is therefore an axiom.

47. Postulate. In geometry a geometric statement admitted without proof to be true is called a *postulate*.

For example, it is so evident that all straight angles are equal, that this statement is a postulate. It is also evident that a straight line may be drawn and that a circle may be described, and these statements are therefore postulates of geometry.

Axioms are therefore general mathematical assumptions, while geometric postulates are the assumptions peculiar to geometry. Postulates and axioms are the assumptions upon which the whole science of mathematics rests.

48. Theorem. A statement to be proved is called a *theorem*.

For example, it is stated in arithmetic that the square on the hypotenuse of a right triangle equals the sum of the squares on the other two sides. This statement is a theorem to be proved in geometry.

49. Problem. A construction to be made so that it shall satisfy certain given conditions is called a *problem*.

For example, required to construct a triangle all of whose sides shall be equal. This construction was made in § 31, Ex. 4, and later it will be proved that the construction was correct.

50. Proposition. A statement of a theorem to be proved or a problem to be solved is called a *proposition*.

In geometry, therefore, a proposition is either a theorem or a problem. We shall find that most of the propositions at first are theorems. After we have proved a number of theorems so that we can prove that the solutions of problems are correct, we shall solve some problems.

51. Corollary. A truth that follows from another with little or no proof is called a *corollary*.

For example, since we admit that all straight angles are equal, it follows as a corollary that all right angles are equal, since a right angle is half of a straight angle.

52. Axioms. The following are the most important axioms used in geometry:

1. *If equals are added to equals the sums are equal.*

2. *If equals are subtracted from equals the remainders are equal.*

3. *If equals are multiplied by equals the products are equal.*

4. *If equals are divided by equals the quotients are equal.*

In division the divisor is never zero.

5. *Like powers or like positive roots of equals are equal.*

We learn from algebra that the square root of 4 is $+2$ or -2, but of course these are not equal. In geometry we shall use only the positive roots.

6. *If unequals are operated on by positive equals in the same way, the results are unequal in the same order.*

Taking $a > b$ and taking x and y as equal positive quantities, this axiom states that

$$a + x > b + y, \quad a - x > b - y, \quad ax > by, \quad \frac{a}{x} > \frac{b}{y}, \text{ etc.}$$

7. *If unequals are added to unequals in the same order, the sums are unequal in the same order; if unequals are subtracted from equals the remainders are unequal in the reverse order.*

If $a > b$, $c > d$, and $x = y$, then $a + c > b + d$, and $x - a < y - b$.

8. *Quantities that are equal to the same quantity or to equal quantities are equal to each other.*

9. *A quantity may be substituted for its equal in an equation or in an inequality.*

Thus if $x = b$ and if $a + x = c$, then $a + b = c$; and if $a + x > c$, then $a + b > c$. Axiom 8 is used so often that it is stated separately, although it is really included in Axiom 9.

10. *If the first of three quantities is greater than the second, and the second is greater than the third, then the first is greater than the third.*

Thus if $a > b$, and if $b > c$, then $a > c$.

11. *The whole is greater than any of its parts, and is equal to the sum of all of its parts.*

53. Postulates. The following are among the most important postulates used in geometry. Others will be introduced as needed.

1. *One straight line and only one can be drawn through two given points.*

2. *A straight line may be produced to any required length.*

To produce AB means to extend it through B; to produce BA means to extend it through A.

A ————————————— B

3. *A straight line is the shortest path between two points.*

4. *A circle may be described with any given point as a center and any given line as a radius.*

5. *Any figure may be moved from one place to another without altering its size or shape.*

6. *All straight angles are equal.*

54. COROLLARY 1. *Two points determine a straight line.*

This is only a brief way of stating Postulate 1.

55. COROLLARY 2. *Two straight lines can intersect in only one point.*

For if they had two points in common they would coincide (Post. 1).

56. COROLLARY 3. *All right angles are equal.*

For all straight angles are equal (Post. 6), and a straight angle (§ 34) is twice a right angle. Hence Axiom 4 applies.

57. COROLLARY 4. *From a given point in a given line only one perpendicular can be drawn to the line.*

For if there could be two perpendiculars to DA at O, as OB and OC, we should have angles AOB and AOC both right angles, which is impossible (§ 56).

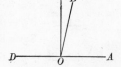

58. COROLLARY 5. *Equal angles have equal complements, equal supplements, and equal conjugates.*

59. COROLLARY 6. *The greater of two angles has the less complement, the less supplement, and the less conjugate.*

EXERCISE 4

1. If $10° + \angle x = 27° \; 30'$, find the value of $\angle x$.

2. If $\angle x + 37° = \frac{1}{2} \angle x + 40°$, find the value of $\angle x$.

3. If $\frac{2}{3} \angle x + \angle b = 5 \angle b$, find the value of $\angle x$.

4. If $\angle x + \angle a = 4 \angle a - \angle x$, find the value of $\angle x$.

Find the value of $\angle x$ in each of the following equations:

5. $\angle x + 13° = 39°$.

6. $\angle x - 17° = 46°$.

7. $2 \angle x = \angle x + 23°$.

8. $5 \angle x = 2 \angle x + 21°$.

9. $4 \angle x = \frac{1}{2} \angle x + 70°$.

10. $\angle x = 0.7 \angle x + 33°$.

11. $\angle x = 0.1 \angle x + 18°$.

12. $\frac{3}{4} \angle x = \frac{1}{2} \angle x + 2\frac{1}{2}°$.

13. $\frac{4}{5} \angle x = 0.1 \angle x + 14°$.

14. $\frac{2}{3} \angle x = \frac{1}{2} \angle x + 2°$.

15. $12 \angle x + 17° = 9 \angle x + 32°$.

16. $5 \angle x - 22° \; 30' = 2 \angle x + 11°$.

17. $51° \; 20' - \frac{2}{3} \angle x = 5° \; 1' + 3 \angle x$.

18. $73° \; 21' \; 4'' - \angle x = 3° \; 3' \; 12'' + 4 \angle x$.

19. If $x + 20° = y$ and $y - 5° = 2 x$, what is the value of x and of y?

Find the value of x and of y in each of the following sets of equations:

20. $x + y = 45°$,
$x - y = 35°$.

21. $x - 8 y = 0°$,
$x + 8 y = 80°$.

22. $2 x + y = 64°$,
$3 x - y = 88°$.

23. $x + 2 y = 21°$,
$x + 3 y = 26° \; 15'$.

24. $x + y = 9° \; 20' \; 15''$,
$2 x - y = 12° \; 25' \; 15''$.

25. $x - y = 5' \; 5''$,
$3 x + 4 y = 14° \; 50' \; 50''$.

26. If $x < 10°$ and $y = 7° \; 30'$, what can be said as to the value of $x + y$?

27. In Ex. 26, what can be said as to the value of $x - y$?

BOOK I

RECTILINEAR FIGURES

PROPOSITION I. THEOREM

60. *If two lines intersect, the vertical angles are equal.*

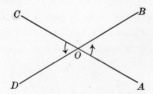

Given the lines *AC* and *BD* intersecting at *O*.

To prove that $\angle AOB = \angle COD.$

Proof. $\angle AOB + \angle BOC = $ a st. $\angle.$ § 43

(The two adjacent angles which one straight line makes with another are together equal to a straight angle.)

Likewise $\angle BOC + \angle COD = $ a st. $\angle.$ § 43

$\therefore \angle AOB + \angle BOC = \angle BOC + \angle COD.$ Post. 6

(All straight angles are equal.)

$\therefore \angle AOB = \angle COD.$ Ax. 2

(If equals are subtracted from equals the remainders are equal.) Q. E. D.

61. Nature of a Proof. From Prop. I it is seen that a theorem has (1) certain things *given ;* (2) a definite thing *to be proved ;* (3) a *proof*, consisting of definite statements, each supported by the authority of a definition, an axiom, a postulate, or some proposition previously proved.

62. **Triangles classified as to Sides.** A triangle is said to be

scalene when no two of its sides are equal;
isosceles when two of its sides are equal;
equilateral when all of its sides are equal.

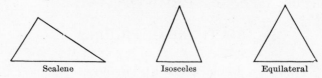

Scalene   Isosceles   Equilateral

63. **Triangles classified as to Angles.** A triangle is said to be

right when one of its angles is a right angle;
obtuse when one of its angles is an obtuse angle;
acute when all of its angles are acute angles;
equiangular when all of its angles are equal.

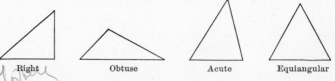

Right   Obtuse   Acute   Equiangular

64. **Corresponding Angles and Sides.** If two triangles have
the angles of the one respectively equal to the angles of the
other, the equal angles are called *corresponding angles,* and the
sides opposite these angles are called *corresponding sides.*

Corresponding parts are also called *homologous parts.*

65. **Square.** A rectilinear figure having four equal sides and
four right angles is called a *square.*

66. **Congruent.** If two figures can be made to coincide in all
their parts, they are said to be *congruent.*

67. Corollary. *Corresponding parts of congruent figures
are equal.*

When equal figures are necessarily congruent, as in the case of angles
or straight lines, the word *equal* is used. For symbols see page vi.

PROPOSITION II. THEOREM

68. *Two triangles are congruent if two sides and the included angle of the one are equal respectively to two sides and the included angle of the other.*

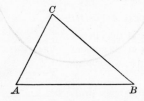 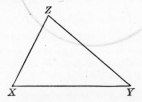

Given the triangles *ABC* and *XYZ*, with *AB* equal to *XY*, *AC* equal to *XZ*, and the angle *A* equal to the angle *X*.

To prove that △ *ABC is congruent to* △ *XYZ.*

Proof. Place the △ *ABC* upon the △ *XYZ* so that *A* shall fall on *X* and *AB* shall fall along *XY*.   Post. 5

(Any figure may be moved from one place to another without altering its size or shape.)

Then *B* will fall on *Y*,

(For AB is given equal to XY.)

AC will fall along *XZ*,

(For ∠A is given equal to ∠X.)

and *C* will fall on *Z*.

(For AC is given equal to XZ.)

∴ *CB* will coincide with *ZY*.   Post. 1

(One straight line and only one can be drawn through two given points.)

∴ the two △ coincide and are congruent, by § 66.   Q.E.D.

69. COROLLARY. *Two right triangles are congruent if the sides of the right angles are equal respectively.*

The right angles are equal (§ 56). How does Prop. II apply?

1. In this figure if $\angle a = 53°$, how many degrees are there in $\angle y$? in $\angle x$? in $\angle z$?

2. In Ex. 1, if $\angle a$ were increased to 89°, what would then be the size of $\angle x$, y, and z?

3. In the square $ABCD$, prove that $AC = BD$.

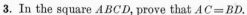

In $\triangle ABC$ and BAD what two sides of the one are known to be equal to what two sides of the other? How about the included angles? Write a complete proof as in Prop. II.

4. If $ABCD$ is a square and P is the midpoint of AB, prove that $PC = PD$.

What triangles should be proved congruent? Can this be done by Prop. II? Write the proof.

5. How many degrees in an angle that equals one fourth of its complement? one tenth of its complement?

6. How many degrees in an angle that equals twice its supplement? one third of its supplement?

7. In the square $ABCD$ the points P, Q, R, S bisect the consecutive sides. Prove that $PQ = QR = RS = SP$.

8. In the square $ABCD$ the point P bisects CD, and BM is made equal to AN, as shown in this figure. Prove that $PM = PN$.

What two sides and included angle of one triangle must be proved equal to what two sides and included angle of another triangle?

9. Prove that to determine the distance AB across a pond one may sight from A across a post P, place a stake at A' making $PA' = AP$, then sight along BP making $PB' = BP$, and finally measure $A'B'$.

70. Drawing the Figures. Directions have already been given (§ 31) for drawing the most common geometric figures. For example, in Prop. II the complete work of drawing $\triangle XYZ$ so that $XY = AB$, $\angle X = \angle A$, and $XZ = AC$, is indicated in the following figures, *the construction lines being dotted*, as is always the case in this book.

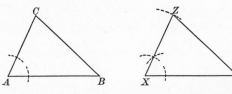

It is desirable to construct such figures accurately, employing compasses and ruler until such time as the use of these instruments is thoroughly understood. Eventually, however, the figures should be rapidly but neatly drawn, free-hand or with the aid of the ruler, as the mathematician usually makes his figures.

71. Designating Corresponding Sides and Angles. It is helpful in propositions concerning equality of figures to check the equal parts so that the eye can follow the proof more easily. Thus it would be convenient to represent the above figures as follows:

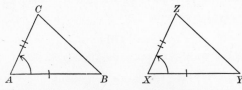

Here AB and XY have one check, AC and XZ two checks, and the equal angles A and X are marked by curved arrows.

If a figure is very complicated, there is sometimes an advantage in using colored crayons or colored pencils, but otherwise this expedient is of little value.

While such figures have some attraction for the eye they are not generally used in practice, one reason being that the student rarely has a supply of colored pencils at hand when studying by himself.

Proposition III. Theorem

72. *Two triangles are congruent if two angles and the included side of the one are equal respectively to two angles and the included side of the other.*

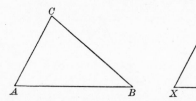

Given the triangles *ABC* and *XYZ*, with angle *A* equal to angle *X*, angle *B* equal to angle *Y*, and with *AB* equal to *XY*.

To prove that △ *ABC is congruent to* △ *XYZ*.

Proof. Place the △ *ABC* upon the △ *XYZ* so that *AB* shall coincide with its equal, *XY*.   Post. 5

(Any figure may be moved from one place to another without altering its size or shape.)

Then *AC* will fall along *XZ* and *BC* along *YZ*.

(For it is given that ∠A = ∠X and ∠B = ∠Y.)

∴ *C* will fall on *Z*.   § 55

(Two straight lines can intersect in only one point.)

∴ the two △ are congruent.   § 66

(If two figures can be made to coincide in all their parts, they are said to be congruent.)   q. e. d.

73. Hypothesis. A supposition made in an argument is called an *hypothesis*.

Thus, where it is said that ∠A = ∠X and ∠B = ∠Y, we might say that this is true "by hypothesis," instead of saying that ∠A is given equal to ∠X, and ∠B is given equal to ∠Y. The word is generally used, however, for an assumption made somewhere *in the proof*.

EXERCISE 6

1. In the square $ABCD$ the point P bisects CD, and PQ and PR are drawn so that $\angle QPC = 30°$ and $\angle RPQ = 120°$. Prove that $PQ = PR$.

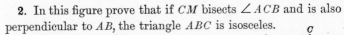

If $\angle QPC = 30°$ and $\angle RPQ = 120°$, what does $\angle DPR$ equal?

In the two triangles what parts are respectively equal, and why?

Write the proof in full.

2. In this figure prove that if CM bisects $\angle ACB$ and is also perpendicular to AB, the triangle ABC is isosceles.

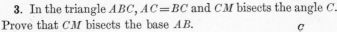

In $\triangle AMC$ and BMC are two angles of the one respectively equal to two angles of the other? Why?

The two triangles have one common side.

Write the proof in full.

3. In the triangle ABC, $AC = BC$ and CM bisects the angle C. Prove that CM bisects the base AB.

4. The triangle ABC has $\angle A$ equal to $\angle B$. The point P bisects AB, and the lines PM and PN are drawn so that $\angle BPM = \angle NPA$. Prove that $BM = AN$.

5. The triangle ABC has $\angle A = \angle B$. The lines AP and BQ are so drawn that $\angle BAP = \angle QBA$. Prove that $AP = BQ$.

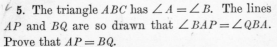

6. Wishing to measure the distance across a river, some boys sighted from A to a point P. They then turned and measured AB at right angles to AP. They placed a stake at O, halfway from A to B, and drew a perpendicular to AB at B. They placed a stake at C, on this

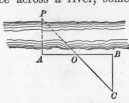

perpendicular, and in line with O and P. They then found the width by measuring BC. Prove that they were right.

Proposition IV. Theorem

74. *In an isosceles triangle the angles opposite the equal sides are equal.*

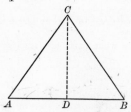

Given the isosceles triangle *ABC*, with *AC* equal to *BC*.

To prove that $\angle A = \angle B$.

Proof. Suppose *CD* drawn so as to bisect $\angle ACB$. Then in the $\triangle ADC$ and BDC,

$$AC = BC, \qquad\qquad \text{Given}$$
$$CD = CD, \qquad\qquad \text{Iden.}$$

(That is, CD is common to the two triangles.)

and $\qquad\qquad \angle ACD = \angle DCB.$ Hyp.

(For CD bisects $\angle ACB$.)

$$\therefore \triangle ADC \text{ is congruent to } \triangle BDC. \qquad \S 68$$

(Two $\triangle$ are congruent if two sides and the included $\angle$ of the one are equal respectively to two sides and the included $\angle$ of the other.)

$$\therefore \angle A = \angle B. \qquad\qquad \S 67$$

(Corresponding parts of congruent figures are equal.)   Q.E.D.

This proposition has long been known as the *Pons asinorum*, or Bridge of Fools (asses). It is attributed to Thales, a Greek philosopher.

In an isosceles triangle the side which is not one of the two equal sides is called the *base*.

75. Corollary. *An equilateral triangle is equiangular.*

Is an equilateral triangle a special kind of isosceles triangle?

EXERCISE 7

1. With the figure of Prop. IV, if $AC = BC$ and CD bisects $\angle C$, prove that CD is $\perp$ to AB.

What angles must be proved to be right angles ? What is a right angle ? Do these angles fulfill the requirements of the definition ?

2. In the adjacent figure $AC = BC$. Prove that $\angle m = \angle n$.

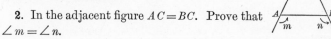

3. In the following figure $AC = BC$ and $AD = BD$. Prove that $\angle CBD = \angle DAC$.

What angles are equal by Prop. IV ? Then what axiom applies ?

4. In the figure of Ex. 3 prove that if a line is drawn from C to D, the $\triangle DBC$ is congruent to the $\triangle DAC$.

5. Two isosceles triangles, ABC and ABD, are constructed on the same side of the common base AB. Prove that $\angle CBD = \angle DAC$.

6. In the figure of Ex. 5 prove that a line drawn through C and D bisects $\angle ADB$.

What two triangles must be proved congruent ?

7. In this figure $AC = BC$ and $AP = BQ$. Prove that $PC = QC$. Also prove that $\angle MPC = \angle CQM$.

8. In this figure, if $AC = BC$, $AP = BQ$, and $PM = QM$, prove that CM is $\perp$ to PQ.

What angles must be proved to be right angles ?

9. In this figure P, Q, and R are mid-points of the sides of the equilateral triangle ABC. Prove that PQR is an equilateral triangle.

Prove that $\triangle APR$, BQP, and CRQ are congruent by using two propositions already proved.

Proposition V. Theorem

76. *If two angles of a triangle are equal, the sides opposite the equal angles are equal, and the triangle is isosceles.*

Given the triangle *ABC*, with the angle *A* equal to the angle *B*.

To prove that $AC = BC$.

Proof. Suppose the second triangle $A'B'C'$ to be an exact reproduction of the given triangle ABC.

Turn the triangle $A'B'C'$ over and place it upon ABC so that B' shall fall on A and A' shall fall on B.   Post. 5

Then $B'A'$ will coincide with AB.   Post. 1

Since $\angle A' = \angle B'$,   Given

and $\angle A = \angle A'$,   Hyp.

$\therefore \angle A = \angle B'$.   Ax. 8

$\therefore B'C'$ will lie along AC.

Similarly $A'C'$ will lie along BC.

Therefore C' will fall on both AC and BC, and hence at their intersection. $\therefore B'C' = AC$.

But $B'C'$ was made equal to BC.

$\therefore AC = BC$, by Ax. 8.   Q.E.D.

77. Corollary. *An equiangular triangle is equilateral.*

78. Kinds of Proof. In the five propositions thus far proved in the text two different kinds of proof have been seen :

(1) *Synthetic.* In Prop. I we put together some known truths in order to obtain a new truth. Such a method of proof is known as the *synthetic method,* and is the most common of all that are used in geometry.

In this method we endeavor simply to find what propositions have already been proved that will lead to the proof of the proposition that is before us. This method was used in all the exercises on pages 28, 31, and 33.

(2) *By superposition.* In Props. II and III we placed one figure on another and then, by synthetic reasoning, showed them to be identically equal. Such proof is known as a proof *by superposition.* Superposition means " placing on," and one figure is said to be superposed on the other.

In Prop. V a special kind of proof by superposition was employed, in which we superpose a figure on its exact duplicate. This special method is rarely used, but in this proposition it materially simplifies the proof.

79. Converse Propositions. If two propositions are so related that what is given in each is what is to be proved in the other, each proposition is called the *converse* of the other.

E.g. in Prop. IV we have given

$$AC = BC, \text{ to prove that } \angle A = \angle B.$$

In Prop. V we have given

$$\angle A = \angle B, \text{ to prove that } AC = BC.$$

Hence Prop. V is the converse of Prop. IV, and Prop. IV is the converse of Prop. V.

Not all converses are true, and hence we have to prove any given converse.

E.g. the converse of the statement "Two right angles are two equal angles" is "Two equal angles are two right angles," and this statement is evidently false.

PROPOSITION VI. THEOREM

80. *Two triangles are congruent if the three sides of the one are equal respectively to the three sides of the other.*

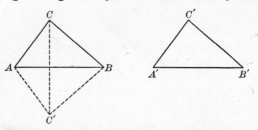

Given the triangles ABC and $A'B'C'$, with AB equal to $A'B'$, AC equal to $A'C'$, and BC equal to $B'C'$.

To prove that $\triangle ABC$ *is congruent to* $\triangle A'B'C'$.

Proof. Let AB and $A'B'$ be the greatest of the sides of the $\triangle$.

Place $\triangle A'B'C'$ next to $\triangle ABC$ so that A' shall fall on A, the side $A'B'$ shall fall along AB, and the vertex C' shall be opposite the vertex C. 　　　　　　　　　　　　Post. 5

Then 　　　　　　　　B' will fall on B.

(For $A'B'$ is given equal to AB.)

Draw CC'.

Since 　　　　　　　　$AC = AC'$, 　　　　　　　　Given

　　　$\therefore \angle ACC' = \angle CC'A$. 　　　　　　§ 74

Since 　　　　　　　　$BC = BC'$, 　　　　　　　　Given

　　　$\therefore \angle C'CB = \angle BC'C$. 　　　　　　§ 74

$\therefore \angle ACC' + \angle C'CB = \angle CC'A + \angle BC'C$. 　　Ax. 1

Hence 　　　　　　$\angle ACB = \angle BC'A$. 　　　　　Ax. 11

(For $\angle ACB$ is made up of $\angle ACC'$ and $\angle C'CB$, and $\angle BC'A$ is made up of $\angle CC'A$ and $\angle BC'C$.)

$\therefore \triangle ABC$ is congruent to $\triangle ABC'$. 　　　　§ 68

$\therefore \triangle ABC$ is congruent to $\triangle A'B'C'$, by Ax. 9. 　**Q.E.D.**

EXERCISE 8

1. Prove that a line from the vertex to the mid-point of the base of an isosceles triangle cuts the triangle into two congruent triangles.

2. Three iron rods are hinged at the extremities, as shown in this figure. Is the figure rigid? Why?

3. Four iron rods are hinged, as shown in this figure. Is the figure rigid? If not, where would you put in the fifth rod to make it rigid? Prove that this would accomplish the result.

4. If two isosceles triangles are constructed on opposite sides of the same base, prove by Prop. VI and § 67 that the line through the vertices bisects the vertical angles.

5. In this figure $AB = AD$ and $CB = CD$. Prove that AC bisects $\angle BAD$ and $\angle DCB$.

6. In § 31, Ex. 8, it was shown how to bisect an angle, this being the figure used. Draw PX and PY, and prove by Prop. VI that PO bisects $\angle AOB$.

7. In a triangle ABC it is known that $AC = BC$. If $\angle A$ and $\angle B$ are both bisected by lines meeting at P, prove that $\triangle ABP$ is isosceles.

8. In this figure it is known that $\angle m = \angle n$. Prove that $AC = BC$.

9. From the vertices A and B of an equilateral triangle lines are drawn to the mid-points of the opposite sides. Prove that these two lines are equal.

In $\triangle ABQ$ and BAP show that the conditions of congruence as stated in Prop. II are fulfilled.

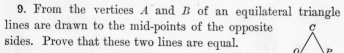

Proposition VII. Theorem

81. *The sum of two lines from a given point to the extremities of a given line is greater than the sum of two other lines similarly drawn, but included by them.*

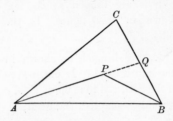

Given *CA* and *CB*, two lines drawn from the point *C* to the extremities of the line *AB*, and *PA* and *PB* two lines similarly drawn, but included by *CA* and *CB*.

To prove that $CA + CB > PA + PB.$

Proof. Produce AP to meet the line CB at Q.   Post. 2

Then $CA + CQ > PA + PQ.$ Post. 3

    (A straight line is the shortest path between two points.)

Likewise $BQ + PQ > PB.$ Post. 3

Add these inequalities, and we have

$$CA + CQ + BQ + PQ > PA + PQ + PB.$$ Ax. 7

(If unequals are added to unequals in the same order, the sums are unequal in the same order.)

Substituting for $CQ + BQ$ its equal CB, we have

$$CA + CB + PQ > PA + PQ + PB.$$ Ax. 9

(A quantity may be substituted for its equal in an equation or in an inequality.)

Taking PQ from each side of the inequality, we have

$$CA + CB > PA + PB, \text{ by Ax. 6.}$$ Q. E. D.

PROPOSITION VIII. THEOREM

82. *Only one perpendicular can be drawn to a given line from a given external point.*

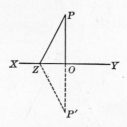

Given a line *XY*, *P* an external point, *PO* a perpendicular to *XY* from *P*, and *PZ* any other line from *P* to *XY*.

To prove that   *PZ is not $\perp$ to XY.*

Proof. Produce *PO* to *P'*, making *OP'* equal to *PO*.   Post. 2

Draw *P'Z*.   Post. 1

By construction *POP'* is a straight line.

$\therefore$ *PZP'* is not a straight line.   Post. 1

Hence $\angle P'ZP$ is not a straight angle.   § 33

Since $\angle POZ$ and ZOP' are rt. $\angle$s,   § 27

$\therefore \angle POZ = \angle ZOP'.$ § 56

Furthermore $PO = OP',$ Hyp.

and $OZ = OZ.$ Iden.

$\therefore \triangle OPZ$ is congruent to $\triangle OP'Z,$ § 68

(*Two $\triangle$ are congruent if two sides and the included $\angle$ of the one are equal respectively to two sides and the included $\angle$ of the other.*)

and $\angle OZP = \angle P'ZO.$ § 67

$\therefore \angle OZP$, the half of $\angle P'ZP$, is not a right angle.   § 34

$\therefore$ *PZ is not $\perp$ to XY*, by § 27.   **Q. E. D.**

Proposition IX. Theorem

83. *Two lines drawn from a point in a perpendicular to a given line, cutting off on the given line equal segments from the foot of the perpendicular, are equal and make equal angles with the perpendicular.*

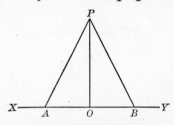

Given *PO* perpendicular to *XY*, and *PA* and *PB* two lines cutting off on *XY* equal segments *OA* and *OB* from *O*.

To prove that $PA = PB$,

and $\angle APO = \angle OPB$.

Proof.　In the △ *AOP* and *BOP*,

　　　　$\angle POA$ and $\angle BOP$ are rt. △.　　　　§ 27

　　　　(*For PO is given* ⊥ *to XY.*)

　　　　∴ $\angle POA = \angle BOP$.　　　　§ 56

　　　　(*All right* △ *are equal.*)

Also　　　　　$OA = OB$,　　　　Given

and　　　　　$PO = PO$.　　　　Iden.

　　　　(*That is, PO is common to the two* △.)

　　　　∴ △ *AOP* is congruent to △ *BOP*.　　　　§ 68

(*Two* △ *are congruent if two sides and the included* ∠ *of the one are equal respectively to two sides and the included* ∠ *of the other.*)

　　　　∴ $PA = PB$,

and　　　　　$\angle APO = \angle OPB$.　　　　§ 67

　　(*Corresponding parts of congruent figures are equal.*)　　**Q. E. D.**

●

Proposition X. Theorem

84. *Of two lines drawn from a point in a perpen-dicular to a given line, cutting off on the given line unequal segments from the foot of the perpendicular, the more remote is the greater.*

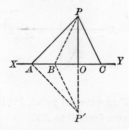

Given *PO* perpendicular to *XY*, *PA* and *PC* two lines drawn from *P* to *XY*, and *OA* greater than *OC*.

To prove that $PA > PC.$

Proof. Take *OB* equal to *OC*, and draw *PB*.

Then $PB = PC.$ § 83

Produce *PO* to *P'*, making $OP' = PO$, and draw *P'A* and *P'B*.

Then $PA = P'A$ and $PB = P'B.$ § 83

But $PA + P'A > PB + P'B.$ § 81

∴ $2PA > 2PB$ and $PA > PB.$ Axs. 9 and 6

∴ $PA > PC$, by Ax. 9.   Q.E.D.

85. Corollary. *Only two equal obliques can be drawn from a given point to a given line, and these cut off equal segments from the foot of the perpendicular.*

Of two unequal lines from a point to a line, the greater cuts off the greater segment from the foot of the perpendicular.

For $PB = PC$, but *PB* cannot equal *PA* (§ 84). The segments *OB* and *OC* are equal, for otherwise *PB* could not equal *PC*.

Proposition XI. Theorem

86. *The perpendicular is the shortest line that can be drawn to a given line from a given external point.*

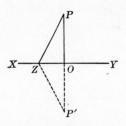

Given a line XY, P an external point, PO the perpendicular, and PZ any other line drawn from P to XY.

To prove that $\qquad\qquad PO < PZ$.

Proof. Produce PO to P', making $OP' = PO$; and draw $P'Z$.

Then $\qquad\qquad\qquad PZ = P'Z$. $\qquad\qquad\qquad$ § 83

(Two lines drawn from a point in a ⊥ to a given line, cutting off on the given line equal segments from the foot of the ⊥, are equal.)

$$\therefore PZ + P'Z = 2\,PZ. \qquad\qquad \text{Ax. 1}$$

Furthermore $\qquad PO + P'O = 2\,PO.$ $\qquad\qquad$ Ax. 1

But $\qquad\qquad PO + P'O < PZ + P'Z.$ $\qquad\qquad$ Post. 3

$$\therefore 2\,PO < 2\,PZ. \qquad\qquad\qquad \text{Ax. 9}$$

$$\therefore PO < PZ, \text{ by Ax. 6.} \qquad\qquad \text{Q. E. D.}$$

87. Hypotenuse. The side opposite the right angle in a right triangle is called the *hypotenuse.*

The other two sides of a right triangle are usually called the *sides.*

88. Distance. The length of the straight line from one point to another is called the *distance* between the points.

The length of the perpendicular from an external point to a line is called the *distance* from the point to the line.

Proposition XII. Theorem

89. *Two right triangles are congruent if the hypotenuse and a side of the one are equal respectively to the hypotenuse and a side of the other.*

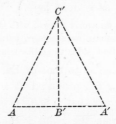

Given the right triangles *ABC* and *A'B'C'*, with the hypotenuse *AC* equal to the hypotenuse *A'C'*, and with *BC* equal to *B'C'*.

To prove that △*ABC is congruent to* △*A'B'C'*.

Proof. Place △*ABC* next to △*A'B'C'*, so that *BC* shall fall along *B'C'*, *B* shall fall on *B'*, and *A* and *A'* shall fall on opposite sides of *B'C'*. Post. 5

Then $\qquad$ *C* will fall on *C'*,

$\qquad$ (*For BC is given equal to B'C'.*)

and $\qquad$ *BA* will fall along *A'B'* produced. § 34

$\qquad$ (*For* ∠*CBA* + ∠*A'B'C'* = *a st.* ∠.)

Since $\qquad$ *AC'* = *A'C'*,

$\qquad$ ∴ *AB'* = *A'B'*. § 85

∴ △*ABC* is congruent to △*A'B'C'*. § 80

(*Two* △ *are congruent if the three sides of the one are equal respectively to the three sides of the other.*) Q. E. D.

90. Corollary. *Two right triangles are congruent if any two sides of the one are equal respectively to the corresponding two sides of the other.*

EXERCISE 9

1. *ABCD* is a square and *M* is the mid-point of *AB*. With *M* as a center an arc is drawn, cutting *BC* at *P* and *AD* at *Q*. Prove that △ *MBP* is congruent to △ *MAQ*, and write the general statement of this theorem without using letters as is done here.

This would read, "If an arc is drawn, with the mid-point of one side of a square as a center, cutting the sides perpendicular to that side, then the triangles cut off by," etc.

2. Draw a figure similar to that of Ex. 1, but take a radius such that the arc cuts *BC* produced at a point above *C*, and *AD* above *D*. Then prove that △ *MBP* is congruent to △ *MAQ*.

3. Prove that if from the point *P* the perpendiculars *PM*, *PN* to the sides of an angle *AOB* are equal, the point *P* lies on the bisector of the angle *AOB*. Write the general statement of this theorem without using letters as is done here.

4. Prove that if the perpendiculars from the mid-point *M* of the base *AB* of a triangle *ABC* to the sides of the triangle are equal, then ∠ *A* = ∠ *B*. What then follows as to the sides *AC* and *BC*? Write the general statement of this theorem without referring to a special figure.

5. Prove that if the perpendiculars from the extremities of the base of a triangle to the other two sides are equal, the triangle is isosceles.

6. Suppose *OY* ⊥ *OX*. With *O* as a center an arc is drawn cutting *OX* at *A* and *OY* at *B*. Then with *A* as a center an arc is drawn cutting *OY* at *P*, and with *B* as a center and the same radius an arc is drawn cutting *OX* at *Q*. Prove that *OP* = *OQ*.

What triangles are congruent by Prop. XII ?

PROPOSITION XIII. THEOREM

91. *Two right triangles are congruent if the hypotenuse and an adjacent angle of the one are equal respectively to the hypotenuse and an adjacent angle of the other.*

Given the right triangles *ABC*, *A'B'C'*, with the hypotenuse *AC* equal to the hypotenuse *A'C'*, and with angle *A* equal to angle *A'*.

To prove that △*ABC is congruent to* △*A'B'C'*.

Proof. Place △*ABC* upon △*A'B'C'* so that *A* shall fall upon *A'* and *AC* shall fall along *A'C'*. Post. 5

Then C will fall on *C'*,

(For AC is given equal to A'C'.)

and *AB* will lie along *A'B'*.

(For ∠A is given equal to ∠A'.)

Then because *C* falls on *C'*,

and ∠*B* and *B'* are rt. ∠s, Given

(Since the ∠ are given as rt. ∠.)

∴ *CB* will coincide with *C'B'*. § 82

(Only one perpendicular can be drawn to a given line from a given external point.)

∴ △*ABC* is congruent to △*A'B'C'*. § 66

(If two figures can be made to coincide in all their parts, they are said to be congruent.) Q. E. D.

Proposition XIV. Theorem

92. *Two lines in the same plane perpendicular to the same line cannot meet however far they are produced.*

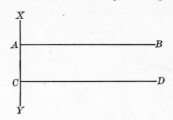

Given the lines *AB* and *CD* perpendicular to *XY* at *A* and *C* respectively.

To prove that AB and CD cannot meet however far they are produced.

Proof. If AB and CD can meet if sufficiently produced, we shall have two perpendicular lines from their point of meeting to the same line.

But this is impossible.   § 82

∴ AB and CD cannot meet.   Q.E.D.

93. Parallel Lines. Lines that lie in the same plane and cannot meet however far produced are called *parallel lines*.

94. Postulate of Parallels. *Through a given point only one line can be drawn parallel to a given line.*

As always in such cases the word *line* means straight line.

95. Corollary 1. *Two lines in the same plane perpendicular to the same line are parallel.*

96. Corollary 2. *Two lines in the same plane parallel to a third line are parallel to each other.*

For if they could meet, we should have two lines through a point parallel to a line. Why is this impossible?

Proposition XV. Theorem

97. *If a line is perpendicular to one of two parallel lines, it is perpendicular to the other also.*

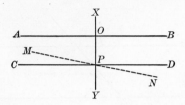

Given *AB* and *CD*, two parallel lines, with *XY* perpendicular to *AB* and cutting *CD* at *P*.

To prove that $\qquad$ *XY is* ⊥ *to CD*.

Proof. Suppose *MN* drawn through *P* ⊥ to *XY*.

Then	*MN* is ‖ to *AB*.	§ 95
But	*CD* is ‖ to *AB*.	Given
	∴ *CD* and *MN* must coincide.	§ 94
But	*XY* is ⊥ to *MN*.	Hyp.
	∴ *XY* is ⊥ to *CD*.	Q. E. D.

98. Transversal. A line that cuts two or more lines is called a *transversal* of those lines.

99. Angles made by a Transversal.
If *XY* cuts *AB* and *CD*, the angles *a, d, g, f* are called *interior* angles; *b, c, h, e* are called *exterior* angles.

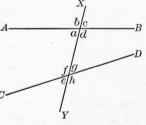

The angles *d* and *f*, and *a* and *g*, are called *alternate-interior* angles; the angles *b* and *h*, and *c* and *e*, are called *alternate-exterior* angles.

The angles *b* and *f*, *c* and *g*, *e* and *a*, *h* and *d*, are called *exterior-interior* angles.

Proposition XVI. Theorem

100. *If two parallel lines are cut by a transversal, the alternate-interior angles are equal.*

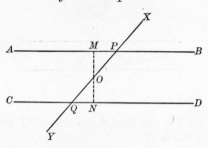

Given *AB* and *CD*, two parallel lines cut by the transversal *XY* in the points *P* and *Q* respectively.

To prove that $\angle APQ = \angle DQP.$

Proof. Through *O*, the mid-point of *PQ*, suppose *MN* drawn ⊥ to *CD*.

Then *MN* is likewise ⊥ to *AB*. § 97

(*A line ⊥ to one of two ∥s is ⊥ to the other.*)

Now △ *PMO* and *QNO* are rt. △. § 63

(*Since ∠ OMP and ONQ are rt. ∠.*)

But $\angle POM = \angle QON,$ § 60

(*If two lines intersect, the vertical ∠ are equal.*)

and $OP = OQ.$ Hyp.

(*For O was taken as the mid-point of PQ.*)

∴ △ *PMO* is congruent to △ *QNO*. § 91

(*Two right ∠ are congruent if the hypotenuse and an adjacent ∠ of the one are equal respectively to the hypotenuse and an adjacent ∠ of the other.*)

∴ $\angle APQ = \angle DQP.$ § 67

(*Corresponding parts of congruent figures are equal.*) **Q.E.D.**

Proposition XVII. Theorem

101. *When two lines in the same plane are cut by a transversal, if the alternate-interior angles are equal, the two lines are parallel.*

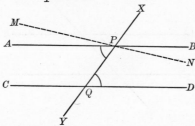

Given the lines **AB** and **CD** cut by the transversal **XY** in the points *P* and *Q* respectively, so as to make the angles *APQ* and *DQP* equal.

To prove that   *AB is* ‖ *to CD*.

Proof. Since we do not know that *AB* is ‖ to *CD*, let us suppose *MN* drawn through *P* ‖ to *CD*.

We shall then prove that *AB* coincides with *MN*.

Now $\angle MPQ = \angle DQP.$ § 100

(If two ‖ lines are cut by a transversal, the alt.-int. ∠s are equal.)

But $\angle APQ = \angle DQP.$ Given

∴ $\angle APQ = \angle MPQ.$ Ax. 8

(Quantities that are equal to the same quantity are equal to each other.)

∴ *AB* and *MN* must coincide.   § 23

(Def. of equal angles.)

But   *MN* is ‖ to *CD*.   Hyp.

(For MN was drawn ‖ to CD.)

∴ *AB*, which coincides with *MN*, is ‖ to *CD*.   **Q.E.D**

This proposition is the converse of Prop. XVI, as defined in § 79.

PROPOSITION XVIII. THEOREM

102. *If two parallel lines are cut by a transversal, the exterior-interior angles are equal.*

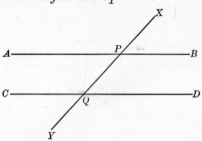

Given *AB* and *CD*, two parallel lines, cut by the transversal *XY* in the points *P* and *Q* respectively.

To prove that $\angle BPX = \angle DQX$.

Proof. $\angle BPX = \angle APQ$.   § 60

                 $\angle APQ = \angle DQX$.   § 100

       $\therefore \angle BPX = \angle DQX$, by Ax. 8.   Q.E.D.

103. COROLLARY 1. *When two lines are cut by a transversal, if the exterior-interior angles are equal, the lines are parallel.*

The proofs of §§ 103 and 105 are similar to that of § 101.

104. COROLLARY 2. *If two parallel lines are cut by a transversal, the two interior angles on the same side of the transversal are supplementary.*

105. COROLLARY 3. *When two lines are cut by a transversal, if two interior angles on the same side of the transversal are supplementary, the lines are parallel.*

106. COROLLARY 4. *If two parallel lines are cut by a transversal, the alternate-exterior angles are equal.*

Proposition XIX. Theorem

107. *The sum of the three angles of a triangle is equal to two right angles.*

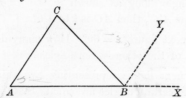

Given the triangle *ABC*.

To prove that $\angle A + \angle B + \angle C = 2$ *rt.* $\angle$*s.*

Proof. Suppose *BY* drawn ∥ to *AC*, and produce *AB* to *X*.

Then $\angle XBY + \angle YBC + \angle CBA = 2$ rt. $\angle$s. §34

(*For a st.* $\angle$ *equals 2 rt.* $\angle$*s.*)

But $\angle A = \angle XBY,$ §102

and $\angle C = \angle YBC.$ §100

$\therefore \angle A + \angle B + \angle C = 2$ rt. $\angle$s, by Ax. 9. Q.E.D.

108. Corollary 1. *If two triangles have two angles of the one equal to two angles of the other, the third angles are equal.*

109. Corollary 2. *In a triangle there can be but one right angle or one obtuse angle.*

110. Exterior Angle. The angle included by one side of a figure and an adjacent side produced is called an *exterior angle.*

In the above figure $\angle XBC$ is an exterior angle, and $\angle$s *A* and *C* are called the *opposite interior angles.*

111. Corollary 3. *An exterior angle of a triangle is equal to the sum of the two opposite interior angles, and is therefore greater than either of them.*

EXERCISE 10

1. Show that if we place a draftsman's triangle against a ruler and draw AC, and move the triangle along as shown in the figure and draw $A'C'$, then AC is ∥ to $A'C'$.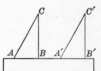

2. In the next figure $x = 60°$. How many degrees in each of the other seven angles?

3. In the next figure representing two pairs of parallel lines certain angles are equal. State these equalities in this form: $a = c = g = e = o = \cdots$, and give the reason in each case.

4. In the figure of Ex. 3 state ten pairs of nonadjacent angles that are supplementary. Thus: $a + h = 180°$ and $d + e = 180°$.

5. In the triangle ABC, $AC = BC$ and DE is drawn parallel to AB. Prove that $CD = CE$. Write a general statement of the theorem.

6. In the next figure AB is parallel to CD, and $\angle APQ$ is half of $\angle QPB$. How many degrees in the various angles?

7. If $\angle YQD = 135°$, how many degrees in the various angles?

8. Let $\angle DQP = x$ and $\angle YQD = y$. Then if $y - x = 100°$, find the value of x and y.

9. Let $\angle CQY = x$ and $\angle XPA = y$. Then if $x = \frac{1}{3} y$, find the value of x and y.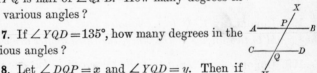

10. In the next figure $x = 72°$ and $x = \frac{2}{3} y$. It is required to know if the lines are parallel, and why.

11. In the figure of Ex. 10 suppose $x = 73°$ and $y - x = 32°$. It is required to know if the lines are parallel, and why.

The three angles of a triangle are x, y, and z. Find the value of z, given the values of x and y as follows :

12. $x = 10°$, $y = 30°$.   **17.** $x = 37°$, $y = 48°$.

13. $x = 20°$, $y = 20°$.   **18.** $x = 63°$, $y = 29°$.

14. $x = 75°$, $y = 50°$.   **19.** $x = 75° \; 29'$, $y = 68° \; 41'$.

15. $x = 38°$, $y = 76°$.   **20.** $x = 82° \; 33'$, $y = 75° \; 48'$.

16. $x = 49°$, $y = 92°$.   **21.** $x = 69° \; 58'$, $y = 82° \; 49'$.

22. In a certain right triangle one angle is 37°. What is the size of the other acute angle?

23. In a certain right triangle one angle is 36° 41'. What is the size of the other acute angle?

24. In a certain right triangle one angle is 29° 48' 56''. What is the size of the other acute angle?

25. In a certain right triangle one acute angle is two thirds of the other. How many degrees are there in each?

26. In a certain right triangle one acute angle is twice as large as the other. How many degrees are there in each?

27. In a certain right triangle the acute angles are $2\,x$ and $5\,x$. Find the value of x and the size of each angle.

28. In a certain triangle one angle is twice as large as another and three times as large as the third. How many degrees are there in each?

29. In a certain isosceles triangle one angle is twice another angle. How many degrees in each of the three angles?

30. In this figure what single angle equals $a + c$? To the sum of what angles is q equal? also r? From these relations find the number of degrees in $p + q + r$.

31. Prove Prop. XIX by first drawing a parallel to AB through C, instead of drawing BY.

Proposition XX. Theorem

112. *The sum of any two sides of a triangle is greater than the third side, and the difference between any two sides is less than the third side.*

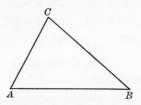

Given the triangle *ABC*, with *AB* the greatest side.

To prove that $BC + CA > AB$, *and* $AB - BC < CA$.

Proof. $BC + CA > AB$.   Post. 3

(A straight line is the shortest path between two points.)

Since $BC + CA > AB$,

        $\therefore CA > AB - BC$;   Ax. 6

or, $AB - BC < CA$.   Q.E.D.

EXERCISE 11

State in what cases it is possible to form triangles with rods of the following lengths, and give the reason:

1. 2 in., 3 in., 4 in.   **4.** 7 in., 10 in., 20 in.

2. 3 in., 4 in., 7 in.   **5.** 8 in., $9\frac{1}{2}$ in., 18 in.

3. 6 in., 7 in., 9 in.   **6.** $9\frac{3}{4}$ in., $10\frac{1}{2}$ in., $12\frac{1}{4}$ in.

7. In this figure prove that $AB + BC > AD + DC$.

Why is $DB + BC > DC$?

What is the result of adding AD to these unequals?

8. How many degrees are there in each angle of an equiangular triangle? Prove it.

Proposition XXI. Theorem

113. *If two sides of a triangle are unequal, the angles opposite these sides are unequal, and the angle opposite the greater side is the greater.*

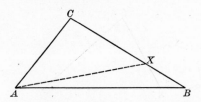

Given the triangle ABC, with BC greater than CA.

To prove that $\angle BAC > \angle B.$

Proof. On CB suppose CX taken equal to CA.

$$\text{Draw } AX. \hspace{3cm} \text{Post. 1}$$

$$\text{Then } \triangle AXC \text{ is isosceles.} \hspace{2cm} \S 62$$

Then $\hspace{2cm} \angle CXA = \angle XAC. \hspace{2cm} \S 74$

(*In an isosceles △ the ⦨ opposite the equal sides are equal.*)

But $\hspace{2cm} \angle CXA > \angle B. \hspace{2cm} \S 111$

(*An exterior ∠ of a △ is greater than either opposite interior ∠.*)

Also $\hspace{2cm} \angle BAC > \angle XAC. \hspace{2cm} \text{Ax. 11}$

(*For ∠XAC is a part of ∠BAC.*)

Substituting in this inequality for $\angle XAC$ its equal, $\angle CXA$, we have the inequality

$$\angle BAC > \angle CXA. \hspace{2cm} \text{Ax. 9}$$

Since $\hspace{2cm} \angle BAC > \angle CXA,$

and $\hspace{2cm} \angle CXA > \angle B,$

$$\therefore \angle BAC > \angle B. \hspace{2cm} \text{Ax. 10}$$

(*If the first of three quantities is greater than the second, and the second is greater than the third, then the first is greater than the third.*) Q. E. D.

Proposition XXII. Theorem

114. *If two angles of a triangle are unequal, the sides opposite these angles are unequal, and the side opposite the greater angle is the greater.*

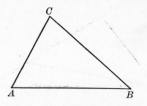

Given the triangle *ABC*, with the angle *A* greater than the angle *B*.

To prove that $BC > CA$.

Proof. Now *BC* is either equal to *CA*, or less than *CA*, or greater than *CA*.

But if *BC* were equal to *CA*,

then the $\angle A$ would be equal to the $\angle B$.　　§ 74

(For they would be ⊿ opposite equal sides.)

And if *CA* were greater than *BC*,

then the $\angle B$ would be greater than the $\angle A$.　§ 113

But if *CA* is not greater than *BC*, this is only another way of saying that *BC* is not less than *CA*.

We have, therefore, two conclusions to be considered,

$$\angle A = \angle B,$$

and 　　　　　　$$\angle A < \angle B.$$

Both these conclusions are contrary to the given fact that the $\angle A$ is greater than the $\angle B$.

Since *BC* cannot be equal to *CA* or less than *CA* without violating the given condition, ∴ $BC > CA$.　　Q.E.D.

This proposition is the converse of Prop. XXI.

Proposition XXIII. Theorem

115. *If two triangles have two sides of the one equal respectively to two sides of the other, but the included angle of the first triangle greater than the included angle of the second, then the third side of the first is greater than the third side of the second.*

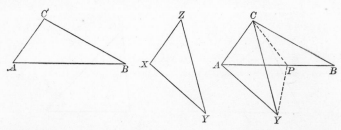

Given the triangles *ABC* and *XYZ*, with *CA* equal to *ZX* and *BC* equal to *YZ*, but with the angle *C* greater than the angle *Z*.

To prove that $AB > XY$.

Proof. Place the △ so that *Z* coincides with *C* and *ZX* falls along *CA*. Then *X* falls on *A*, since *ZX* is given equal to *CA*, and *ZY* falls within ∠ *ACB*, since ∠ *C* is given greater than ∠ *Z*.

Suppose *CP* drawn to bisect the ∠ *YCB*, and draw *YP*.

Then since	$CP = CP,$	Iden.
	$CY = CB,$	Given
and	$\angle YCP = \angle PCB,$	Hyp.
	$\therefore \triangle PYC$ is congruent to $\triangle PBC.$	§ 68
	$\therefore PY = PB.$	§ 67
Now	$AP + PY > AY.$	Post. 3
	$\therefore AP + PB > AY.$	Ax. 9
	$\therefore AB > AY.$	Ax. 11
	$\therefore AB > XY,$ by Ax. 9.	Q. E. D.

Proposition XXIV. Theorem

116. *If two triangles have two sides of the one equal respectively to two sides of the other, but the third side of the first triangle greater than the third side of the second, then the angle opposite the third side of the first is greater than the angle opposite the third side of the second.*

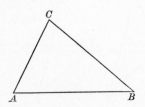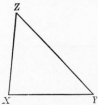

Given the triangles *ABC* and *XYZ*, with *CA* equal to *ZX* and *BC* equal to *YZ*, but with *AB* greater than *XY*.

To prove that the ∠ *C is greater than the* ∠ *Z.*

Proof. Now the ∠ *C* is either equal to the ∠ *Z*, or less than the ∠ *Z*, or greater than the ∠ *Z*.

But if the ∠ *C* were equal to the ∠ *Z*,

then the △ *ABC* would be congruent to the △ *XYZ*,　§ 68

(*For it would have two sides and the included ∠ of the one equal respectively to two sides and the included ∠ of the other.*)

and *AB* would be equal to *XY*.　　　　　§ 67

And if the ∠ *C* were less than the ∠ *Z*,

then *AB* would be less than *XY*.　　　§ 115

Both these conclusions are contrary to the given fact that *AB* is greater than *XY*.

$$\therefore \angle C > \angle Z.$$　　　Q.E.D.

This proposition is the converse of Prop. XXIII.

117. Quadrilateral. A portion of a plane bounded by four straight lines is called a *quadrilateral*.

118. Kinds of Quadrilaterals. A quadrilateral may be

a *trapezoid*, having two sides parallel;

a *parallelogram*, having the opposite sides parallel.

If the nonparallel sides are equal, a trapezoid is called *isosceles*.
A quadrilateral with no two sides parallel is called a *trapezium*.

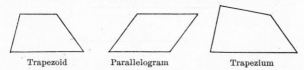

Trapezoid   Parallelogram   Trapezium

119. Kinds of Parallelograms. A parallelogram may be

a *rectangle*, having its angles all right angles;

a *rhombus*, having its sides all equal.

A parallelogram with all its angles oblique is called a *rhomboid*.

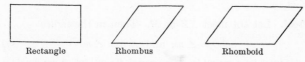

Rectangle   Rhombus   Rhomboid

120. Base. The side upon which a figure is supposed to rest is called the *base*.

If a quadrilateral has a side parallel to the base, this is called the *upper base*, the other being called the *lower base*.

In an isosceles triangle the vertex formed by the equal sides is taken as the *vertex* of the triangle, and the side opposite this vertex is taken as the *base* of the triangle.

121. Altitude. The perpendicular distance between the bases of a parallelogram or trapezoid is called the *altitude*.

The perpendicular distance from the vertex of a triangle to the base is called the *altitude* of the triangle.

122. Diagonal. The straight line joining two nonconsecutive vertices of any figure is called a *diagonal*.

Proposition XXV. Theorem

123. *Two angles whose sides are parallel each to each are either equal or supplementary.*

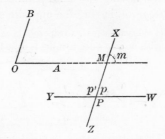

Given the angle *AOB* and the lines *WY* and *XZ* parallel to the sides and intersecting at *P*, the figure being lettered as shown.

To prove that $\angle p = \angle O$, *and that* $\angle p'$ *is supplementary to* $\angle O$.

Proof. Let *OA* meet *XZ* at *M*. Then in the figure

$$\angle O = \angle m, \text{ and } \angle p = \angle m. \qquad \text{§ 102}$$

(*If two ‖ lines are cut by a transversal, the ext.-int.* ∡ *are equal.*)

$$\therefore \angle p = \angle O. \qquad \text{Ax. 8}$$

Also $\angle p'$ is the supplement of $\angle p$.   § 42

$\therefore \angle p'$ is supplementary to $\angle O$, by § 58.   Q.E.D.

If the sides of two angles are parallel each to each, under what circumstances are the angles equal, and under what circumstances are they supplementary ?

124. Corollary. *The opposite angles of a parallelogram are equal, and any two consecutive angles are supplementary.*

Draw the figure and explain how it is known that any angle is the supplement of its consecutive angle. If two opposite angles are supplements of the same angle, show that § 58 applies.

Proposition XXVI. Theorem

125. *The opposite sides of a parallelogram are equal.*

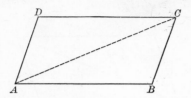

Given the parallelogram *ABCD*.

To prove that $BC = AD$, *and* $AB = DC$.

Proof. Draw the diagonal AC.

In the $\triangle ABC$ and CDA,

$$AC = AC, \qquad\qquad \text{Iden.}$$
$$\angle BAC = \angle DCA,$$
and $\qquad\qquad \angle ACB = \angle CAD. \qquad\qquad \text{§ 100}$

$\therefore \triangle ABC$ is congruent to $\triangle CDA$. § 72

$\therefore BC = AD$, and $AB = DC$, by § 67. Q. E. D.

126. Corollary 1. *A diagonal divides a parallelogram into two congruent triangles.*

Upon what theorem does this depend?

127. Corollary 2. *Segments of parallel lines cut off by parallel lines are equal.*

How does this follow from the proposition?

128. Corollary 3. *Two parallel lines are everywhere equally distant from each other.*

If *AB* and *CD* are parallel, what can be said of ⊥ dropped from *any* points in *AB* to *CD* (§ 127)? Hence what may be said of *all* points in *AB* with respect to their distance from *CD*?

Proposition XXVII. Theorem

129. *If the opposite sides of a quadrilateral are equal, the figure is a parallelogram.*

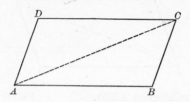

Given the quadrilateral *ABCD*, having *BC* equal to *AD*, and *AB* equal to *DC*.

To prove that the quadrilateral ABCD is a parallelogram.

Proof.   Draw the diagonal *AC*.

In the △ *ABC* and *CDA*,

$$BC = AD,$$ Given

$$AB = DC,$$ Given

and $$AC = AC.$$ Iden.

$$\therefore \triangle ABC \text{ is congruent to } \triangle CDA.$$ § 80

(*Two △ are congruent if the three sides of the one are equal respectively to the three sides of the other.*)

$$\therefore \angle BAC = \angle DCA,$$

and $$\angle ACB = \angle CAD.$$ § 67

$$\therefore AB \text{ is } \parallel \text{ to } DC,$$

and $$BC \text{ is } \parallel \text{ to } AD.$$ § 101

(*When two lines in the same plane are cut by a transversal, if the alt.-int. △ are equal, the two lines are ∥.*)

$$\therefore \text{ the quadrilateral } ABCD \text{ is a } \square, \text{ by § 118.}$$ Q.E.D.

This proposition is the converse of Prop. XXVI.

Proposition XXVIII. Theorem

130. *If two sides of a quadrilateral are equal and parallel, then the other two sides are equal and parallel, and the figure is a parallelogram.*

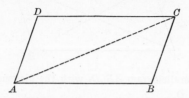

Given the quadrilateral *ABCD*, having *AB* equal and parallel to *DC*.

To prove that the quadrilateral ABCD is a parallelogram.

Proof. Draw the diagonal *AC*.

In the △ *ABC* and *CDA*,

$$AC = AC, \qquad\qquad \text{Iden.}$$
$$AB = DC, \qquad\qquad \text{Given}$$
and $\qquad\qquad \angle BAC = \angle DCA. \qquad\qquad$ § 100

(*If two ‖ lines are cut by a transversal, the alt.-int. △ are equal.*)

∴ △ *ABC* is congruent to △ *CDA.* § 68

(*Two △ are congruent if two sides and the included ∠ of the one are equal respectively to two sides and the included ∠ of the other.*)

$$\therefore BC = AD,$$
and $\qquad\qquad \angle ACB = \angle CAD. \qquad\qquad$ § 67
$$\therefore BC \text{ is ‖ to } AD. \qquad\qquad$$ § 101

(*When two lines in the same plane are cut by a transversal, if the alt.-int. △ are equal, the two lines are ‖.*)

But $\qquad\qquad AB$ is ‖ to *DC.* $\qquad\qquad$ Given

∴ the quadrilateral *ABCD* is a ☐, by § 118. **Q. E. D.**

PROPOSITION XXIX. THEOREM

131. *The diagonals of a parallelogram bisect each other.*

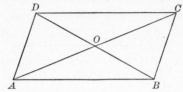

Given the parallelogram *ABCD*, with the diagonals *AC* and *BD* intersecting at *O*.

To prove that $AO = OC,$

and $BO = OD.$

Proof. If we can show that the △ *ABO* is congruent to the △ *CDO*, or that the △ *BCO* is congruent to the △ *DAO*, the proposition is evidently proved, since the corresponding sides of the congruent triangles will be equal.

Now in the ⧍ *ABO* and *CDO,*

$$AB = CD, \qquad\qquad\qquad § 125$$

(*The opposite sides of a □ are equal.*)

$$\angle BAO = \angle DCO,$$

and $\angle OBA = \angle ODC. \qquad\qquad § 100$

(*If two parallel lines are cut by a transversal, the alternate-interior angles are equal.*)

$$\therefore △ ABO \text{ is congruent to } △ CDO. \qquad § 72$$

(*Two ⧍ are congruent if two ⦞ and the included side of the one are equal respectively to two ⦞ and the included side of the other.*)

$$\therefore AO = OC,$$

and $BO = OD. \qquad\qquad § 67$

(*Corresponding parts of congruent ⧍ are equal.*)   Q. E. D.

⌐Proposition XXX. Theorem

132. *Two parallelograms are congruent if two sides and the included angle of the one are equal respectively to two sides and the included angle of the other.*

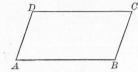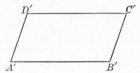

Given the parallelograms *ABCD* **and** *A'B'C'D'*, **with** *AB* **equal to** *A'B'*, *AD* **to** *A'D'*, **and angle** *A* **to angle** *A'*.

To prove that   the ▱ *are congruent.*

Proof. Place the ▱ *ABCD* upon the ▱ *A'B'C'D'* so that *AB* shall fall upon and coincide with its equal, *A'B'*.   Post. 5

Then *AD* will fall along *A'D'*,

(*For* ∠ *A is given equal to* ∠ *A'.*)

and *D* will fall on *D'*.

(*For AD is given equal to A'D'.*)

Now *DC* and *D'C'* are both ∥ to *A'B'* and are drawn through *D'*.

∴ *DC* will fall along *D'C'*.   § 94

(*Through a given point only one line can be drawn* ∥ *to a given line.*)

Also *BC* and *B'C'* are both ∥ to *A'D'* and are drawn through *B'*.

∴ *BC* will fall along *B'C'*.   § 94

∴ *C* will fall on *C'*.   § 55

∴ the two ▱ coincide and are congruent, by § 66.   Q.E.D.

133. Corollary. *Two rectangles having equal bases and equal altitudes are congruent.*

How is this shown to be a special case under the above proposition? What sides are equal, and what included angles are equal?

Proposition XXXI. Theorem

134. *If three or more parallels intercept equal segments on one transversal, they intercept equal segments on every transversal.*

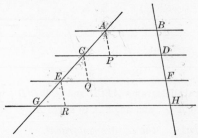

Given the parallels *AB*, *CD*, *EF*, *GH*, intercepting equal segments *BD*, *DF*, *FH* on the transversal *BH*, and intercepting the segments *AC*, *CE*, *EG* on another transversal.

To prove that $AC = CE = EG.$

Proof. Suppose *AP*, *CQ*, and *ER* drawn ∥ to *BH*.

$\angle APC, CQE, ERG = \angle BDC, DFE, FHG$ respectively.	§ 102
But $\angle BDC, DFE, FHG$ are equal.	§ 102
∴ $\angle APC, CQE, ERG$ are equal.	Ax. 8
AP, *CQ*, *ER* are parallel.	§ 96
Also $\angle CAP, ECQ, GER$ are equal.	§ 102
Now $AP = BD, CQ = DF, ER = FH.$	§ 127

(Segments of parallels cut off by parallels are equal.)

But	$BD = DF = FH.$	Given
	∴ $AP = CQ = ER.$	Ax. 8
∴ $\triangle CPA, EQC,$ and GRE are congruent.		§ 72
∴ $AC = CE = EG$, by § 67.		Q.E.D.

135. COROLLARY 1. *If a line is parallel to one side of a triangle and bisects another side, it bisects the third side also.*

Let DE be ‖ to BC and bisect AB. Suppose a line is drawn through A ‖ to BC. Then how do we know this line to be ‖ to DE? Since it is given that the three ‖s intercept equal segments on the transversal AB, what can we say of the intercepted segments on AC? What can we then say that DE does to AC?

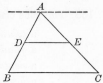

Write the proof of this corollary in full.

136. COROLLARY 2. *The line which joins the mid-points of two sides of a triangle is parallel to the third side, and is equal to half the third side.*

A line DE drawn through the mid-point of AB, ‖ to BC, divides AC in what way (§ 135)? Therefore the line joining the mid-points of AB and AC coincides with this parallel and is ‖ to BC. Also since EF drawn ‖ to AB bisects AC, how does it divide BC? What does this prove as to the relation of BF, FC, and BC? Since $BFED$ is a ▱ (§ 118), what do we know as to the equality of DE, BF, and $\frac{1}{2}BC$?

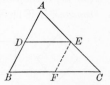

Write the proof of this corollary in full.

137. COROLLARY 3. *The line joining the mid-points of the nonparallel sides of a trapezoid is parallel to the bases and is equal to half the sum of the bases.*

Draw the diagonal DB. In the $\triangle ABD$ join E, the mid-point of AD, to F, the mid-point of DB. Then, by § 136, what relations exist between EF and AB? In the $\triangle DBC$ join F to G, the mid-point of BC. Then what relations exist between FG and DC? Since this relation exists, what relation exists between AB and FG? But only one line can be drawn through F ‖ to AB (§ 94). Therefore FG is the prolongation of EF. Hence EFG is parallel to AB and CD, and equal to $\frac{1}{2}(AB + DC)$.

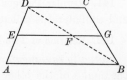

Write the proof of this corollary in full.

138. Polygon. A portion of a plane bounded by a broken line is called a *polygon*.

The terms *sides, perimeter, angles, vertices,* and *diagonals* are employed in the usual sense in connection with polygons in general.

139. Polygons classified as to Sides. A polygon is

a *triangle*, if it has three sides;
a *quadrilateral*, if it has four sides;
a *pentagon*, if it has five sides;
a *hexagon*, if it has six sides.

These names are sufficient for most cases. The next few names in order are *heptagon, octagon, nonagon, decagon, undecagon, dodecagon*.

A polygon is *equilateral*, if all of its sides are equal.

140. Polygons classified as to Angles. A polygon is

equiangular, if all of its angles are equal;
convex, if each of its angles is less than a straight angle;
concave, if it has an angle greater than a straight angle.

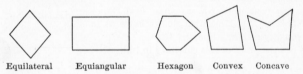

Equilateral   Equiangular   Hexagon   Convex   Concave

An angle of a polygon greater than a straight angle is called a *reëntrant angle*. When the term *polygon* is used, a convex polygon is understood.

141. Regular Polygon. A polygon that is both equiangular and equilateral is called a *regular polygon*.

142. Relation of Two Polygons. Two polygons are

mutually equiangular, if the angles of the one are equal to the angles of the other respectively, taken in the same order;

mutually equilateral, if the sides of the one are equal to the sides of the other respectively, taken in the same order;

congruent, if mutually equiangular and mutually equilateral, since they then can be made to coincide.

PROPOSITION XXXII. THEOREM

143. *The sum of the interior angles of a polygon is equal to two right angles, taken as many times less two as the figure has sides.*

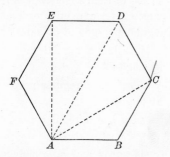

Given the polygon *ABCDEF*, having *n* sides.

To prove that the sum of the interior $\angle = (n-2)\,2$ rt. $\angle$.

Proof. From A draw the diagonals AC, AD, AE.

The sum of the $\angle$ of the $\triangle$ is equal to the sum of the $\angle$ of the polygon.   Ax. 11

Now there are $(n-2)$ $\triangle$.

(*For there is one $\triangle$ for each side except the two sides adjacent to A.*)

The sum of the $\angle$ of each $\triangle = 2$ rt. $\angle$.   § 107

∴ the sum of the $\angle$ of the $(n-2)$ $\triangle$, that is, the sum of the $\angle$ of the polygon, is equal to $(n-2)\,2$ rt. $\angle$, by Ax. 3.   Q.E.D.

144. COROLLARY 1. *The sum of the angles of a quadrilateral equals four right angles; and if the angles are all equal, each is a right angle.*

145. COROLLARY 2. *Each angle of a regular polygon of n sides is equal to $\dfrac{2\,(n-2)}{n}$ right angles.*

EXERCISE 12

1. What is the sum of the angles of (*a*) a pentagon? (*b*) a hexagon? (*c*) a heptagon? (*d*) an octagon? (*e*) a decagon? (*f*) a dodecagon? (*g*) a polygon of 24 sides?

2. What is the size of each angle of (*a*) a regular pentagon? (*b*) a regular hexagon? (*c*) a regular octagon? (*d*) a regular decagon? (*e*) a regular polygon of 32 sides?

3. How many sides has a regular polygon, each angle of which is $1\frac{3}{4}$ right angles?

4. How many sides has a regular polygon, each angle of which is $1\frac{3}{7}$ right angles?

5. How many sides has a regular polygon, each angle of which is 108°?

6. How many sides has a regular polygon, each angle of which is 140°?

7. How many sides has a regular polygon, each angle of which is 156°?

8. Four of the angles of a pentagon are 120°, 80°, 90°, and 100° respectively. Find the fifth angle.

9. Five of the angles of a hexagon are 100°, 120°, 130°, 150°, and 90° respectively. Find the sixth angle.

10. The angles of a quadrilateral are x, $2x$, $2x$, and $3x$. How many degrees are there in each?

11. The angles of a quadrilateral are so related that the second is twice the first, the third three times the first, and the fourth four times the first. How many degrees in each?

12. The angles of a hexagon are x, $2\frac{1}{2}x$, $3\frac{1}{2}x$, $2x$, $2x$, and x. How many degrees are there in each?

13. The sum of two angles of a triangle is 100° and their difference is 40°. How many degrees are there in each of the three angles of the triangle?

Proposition XXXIII. Theorem

146. *The sum of the exterior angles of a polygon, made by producing each of its sides in succession, is equal to four right angles.*

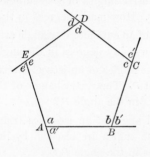

Given the polygon *ABCDE*, having its *n* sides produced in succession.

To prove that the sum of the exterior $\angle = 4$ rt. $\angle$.

Proof. Denote the interior $\angle$ of the polygon by a, b, c, d, e, and the corresponding exterior $\angle$ by a', b', c', d', e'.

Then, considering each pair of adjacent angles,

$$\angle a + \angle a' = \text{a st. } \angle,$$

and $$\angle b + \angle b' = \text{a st. } \angle. \qquad \S 43$$

(*The two adjacent $\angle$ which one straight line makes with another are together equal to a straight $\angle$.*)

In like manner, each pair of adj. $\angle =$ a st. $\angle$.

But the polygon has *n* sides and *n* angles.

Therefore the sum of the interior and exterior $\angle$ is equal to *n* st. $\angle$, or $2n$ rt. $\angle$. \qquad Ax. 3

But the sum of the interior $\angle = (n-2)\, 2$ rt. $\angle$ \qquad § 143

$$= 2n \text{ rt. } \angle - 4 \text{ rt. } \angle.$$

$\therefore$ the sum of the exterior $\angle = 4$ rt. $\angle$, by Ax. 2. **Q.E.D.**

EXERCISE 13

1. An exterior angle of a triangle is 130° and one of the opposite interior angles is 52°. Find the number of degrees in each angle of the triangle.

2. Two consecutive angles of a rectangle are bisected by lines meeting at P. How many degrees in the angle P?

3. Two angles of an equilateral triangle are bisected by lines meeting at P. How many degrees in the angle P?

4. The two base angles of an isosceles triangle are bisected by lines meeting at P. The vertical angle of the triangle is 30°. How many degrees in the angle P?

5. The vertical angle of an isosceles triangle is 40°. This and one of the base angles are bisected by lines meeting at P. How many degrees in the angle P?

6. One exterior angle of a parallelogram is one eighth of the sum of the four exterior angles. How many degrees in each angle of the parallelogram?

7. How many degrees in each exterior angle of a regular hexagon? of a regular octagon?

8. In a right triangle one acute angle is twice the other. How many degrees in each exterior angle of the triangle?

9. Make out a table showing the number of degrees in each interior angle and each exterior angle of regular polygons of three, four, five, ⋯, ten sides.

10. If the diagonals of a quadrilateral bisect each other, the figure is a parallelogram.

11. In this parallelogram $ABCD$, $AP = CR$, and $BQ = DS$. Prove that $PQRS$ is also a parallelogram.

12. If the mid-points of the sides of a parallelogram are connected in order, the resulting figure is also a parallelogram.

147. Locus. The path of a point that moves in accordance with certain given geometric conditions is called the *locus* of the point.

Thus, considering only figures in a plane, a point at a given distance from a given line of indefinite length is evidently in one of two lines parallel to the given line and at the given distance from it. Thus, if *A B* is the given line and *d* the given distance, the locus is evidently the pair of parallel lines *XY* and *X'Y'*.

The locus of a point in a plane at a given distance *r* from a given point *O* is evidently the circle described about *O* as a center with a radius *r*.

The plural of *locus* (a Latin word meaning "place") is *loci* (pronounced lō-sī).

We may think of the locus as the *place* of all points that satisfy certain given geometric conditions, and speak of the locus of points. Both expressions, *locus of a point* and *locus of points*, are used in mathematics.

EXERCISE 14

State without proof the following loci in a plane:

1. The locus of a point 2 in. from a fixed point *O*.

2. The locus of the tip of the minute hand of a watch.

3. The locus of the center of the hub of a carriage wheel moving straight ahead on a level road.

4. The locus of a point 1 in. from each of two parallel lines that are 2 in. apart.

5. The locus of a point on this page and 1 in. from the edge.

6. The locus of the point of a round lead pencil as it rolls along a desk.

7. The locus of the tips of a pair of shears as they open, provided the fulcrum (bolt or screw) remains always fixed in one position.

8. The locus of the center of a circle that rolls around another circle, always just touching it.

148. Proof of a Locus. To prove that a certain line or group of lines is the locus of a point that fulfills a given condition, it is necessary and sufficient to prove two things:

1. *That any point in the supposed locus satisfies the condition.*

2. *That any point outside the supposed locus does not satisfy the given condition.*

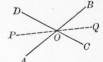

For example, if we wish to find the locus of a point equidistant from these intersecting lines AB, CD, it is not sufficient to prove that any point on the angle-bisector PQ is equidistant from AB and CD, because this may be only part of the locus. It is necessary to prove that no point outside of PQ satisfies the condition. In fact, in this case there is another line in the locus, the bisector of the $\angle BOD$, as will be shown in § 152.

149. Perpendicular Bisector. A line that bisects a given line and is perpendicular to it is called the *perpendicular bisector* of the line.

EXERCISE 15

Draw the following loci, giving no proofs:

1. The locus of a point $\frac{1}{4}$ in. below the base of a given triangle ABC.

2. The locus of a point $\frac{1}{2}$ in. from a given line AB.

3. The locus of a point 1 in. from a given point O.

4. The locus of a point $\frac{1}{2}$ in. outside the circle described about a given point O with a radius $1\frac{1}{2}$ in.

5. The locus of a point $\frac{1}{2}$ in. within the circle described about a given point O with a radius $1\frac{1}{2}$ in.

6. The locus of a point $\frac{1}{2}$ in. from the circle described about a given point O with a radius $1\frac{1}{2}$ in.

7. The locus of a point $\frac{1}{2}$ in. from each of two given parallel lines that are 1 in. apart.

Proposition XXXIV. Theorem

150. *The locus of a point equidistant from the extremities of a given line is the perpendicular bisector of that line.*

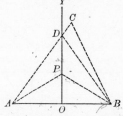

Given *YO*, the perpendicular bisector of the line *AB*.

To prove that YO is the locus of a point equidistant from A and B.

Proof. Let *P* be any point in *YO*, and *C* any point not in *YO*.

Draw the lines *PA*, *PB*, *CA*, and *CB*.

Since	$AO = BO,$	Given
and	$OP = OP,$	Iden.

$\therefore$ rt. $\triangle AOP$ is congruent to rt. $\triangle BOP$.   § 90

$\therefore PA = PB.$ § 67

Let *CA* cut the $\perp$ at *D*, and draw *DB*.

Then, as above,	$DA = DB.$	
But	$CB < CD + DB.$	Post. 3

$\therefore CB < CD + DA.$ Ax. 9

$\therefore CB < CA.$ Ax. 11

$\therefore$ *YO* is the required locus, by § 148.   Q.E.D.

151. Corollary. *Two points each equidistant from the extremities of a line determine the perpendicular bisector of the line.*

Proposition XXXV. Theorem

152. *The locus of a point equidistant from two given intersecting lines is a pair of lines bisecting the angles formed by those lines.*

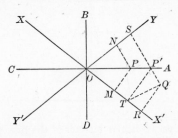

Given *XX'* and *YY'* intersecting at *O*, *AC* the bisector of angle *X'OY*, and *BD* the bisector of angle *YOX*.

To prove that the pair of lines AC and BD is the locus of a point equidistant from XX' and YY'.

Proof. Let *P* be any point on *AC* or *BD*, and *Q* any point not on *AC* or *BD*. Let *PM* and *QR* be ⊥ to *XX'*, *PN* and *QS* to *YY'*.

Since	$\angle MOP = \angle PON$,	Given
and	$OP = OP$,	Iden.
	∴ rt. △ *OMP* is congruent to rt. △ *ONP*.	§ 91
	∴ $PM = PN$.	§ 67

Let *QS* cut *AO* at *P'*. Draw *P'T* ⊥ to *XX'*, and draw *QT*.

Then, as above,	$P'T = P'S$.	
But	$P'T + P'Q > QT$,	Post. 3
and	$QT > QR$.	§ 86
	∴ $P'T + P'Q > QR$.	Ax. 10
Substituting,	$P'S + P'Q > QR$, or $QS > QR$.	Ax. 9

∴ the pair of lines is the required locus, by § 148.   Q.E.D.

153. The Synthetic Method of Proof. The method of proof in which known truths are put together in order to obtain a new truth is called the *synthetic method*.

This is the method used in most of the theorems already given. The proposition usually suggests some known propositions already proved, and from these we proceed to the proof required. The exercises on this page and on pages 78 and 79 may be proved by the synthetic method.

154. Concurrent Lines. If two or more lines pass through the same point, they are called *concurrent lines*.

155. Median. A line from any vertex of a triangle to the mid-point of the opposite side is called a *median* of the triangle.

EXERCISE 16

1. If two triangles have two sides of the one equal respectively to two sides of the other, and the angles opposite two equal sides equal, the angles opposite the other two equal sides are equal or supplementary, and if equal the triangles are congruent.

Let $AC = A'C'$, $BC = B'C'$, and $\angle B = \angle B'$.

Place $\triangle A'B'C'$ on $\triangle ABC$ so that $B'C'$ shall coincide with BC, and $\angle A'$ and $\angle A$ shall be on the same side of BC.

Since $\angle B' = \angle B$, $B'A'$ will fall along what line ? Then A' will fall at A or at some other point in BA, as D. If A' falls at A, what do we know about the congruency of the ▵ $A'B'C'$ and ABC ?

If A' falls at D, what about the congruency of the ▵ $A'B'C'$ and DBC ?
Since $CD = C'A' = CA$, what about the relation of $\angle A$ to $\angle CDA$?
Then what about the relation of the ▵ CDA and BDC ?
Then what about the relation of the ▵ A and BDC ?

Draw figures and show that the triangles are congruent :

1. If the given angles B and B' are both right or both obtuse.
2. If the angles A and A' are both acute, both right, or both obtuse.
3. If AC and $A'C'$ are not less than BC and $B'C'$ respectively.

2. The bisectors of the angles of a triangle are concurrent in a point equidistant from the sides of the triangle.

The bisectors of two angles, as AD and BE, intersect as at O. Why? Now show that O is equidistant from AC and AB, also from BC and AB, and hence from AC and BC. Therefore, where does O lie with respect to the bisector CF?

This point O is called the *incenter* of the triangle.

3. The perpendicular bisectors of the sides of a triangle are concurrent in a point equidistant from the vertices.

The $\perp$ bisectors of two sides, as QQ' and RR', intersect as at O. Why? Now show that O is equidistant from B and C, also from C and A, and hence from A and B. Therefore, where does O lie with respect to the $\perp$ bisector PP'?

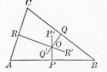

This point O is called the *circumcenter* of the triangle.

4. The perpendiculars from the vertices of a triangle to the opposite sides are concurrent.

Let the ⟂s be AQ, BR, and CP. Through A, B, C suppose $B'C'$, $C'A'$, and $A'B'$ drawn ∥ to CB, AC, and BA respectively. Now show that $C'A = BC = AB'$. In the same way, what are the mid-points of $C'A'$ and $A'B'$? How does this prove that AQ, BR, and CP are the $\perp$ bisectors of the sides of the $\triangle A'B'C'$? Proceed as in Ex. 3.

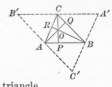

This point O is called the *orthocenter* of the triangle.

5. The medians of a triangle are concurrent in a point two thirds of the distance from each vertex to the middle of the opposite side.

Two medians, as AQ and CP, meet as at O. If Y is the mid-point of AO, and X of CO, show that YX and PQ are ∥ to AC and equal to $\frac{1}{2} AC$. Then show that $AY = YO = OQ$, and $CX = XO = OP$. Hence *any* median cuts off on *any* other median what part of the distance from the vertex to the mid-point of the opposite side?

This point O is called the *centroid* of the triangle.

6. The bisectors of two vertical angles are in the same straight line.

7. The bisector of one of two vertical angles bisects the other.

8. The bisectors of two supplementary adjacent angles are perpendicular to each other.

9. The bisectors of the two pairs of vertical angles formed by two intersecting lines are perpendicular to each other.

10. If the bisectors of two adjacent angles are perpendicular to each other, the adjacent angles are supplementary.

11. If an angle is bisected, and if a line is drawn through the vertex perpendicular to the bisector, this line forms equal angles with the sides of the given angle.

12. The bisector of the vertical angle of an isosceles triangle bisects the base and is perpendicular to the base.

13. The perpendicular bisector of the base of an isosceles triangle passes through the vertex and bisects the angle at the vertex.

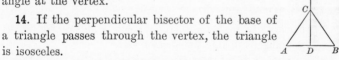

14. If the perpendicular bisector of the base of a triangle passes through the vertex, the triangle is isosceles.

15. Any point in the bisector of the vertical angle of an isosceles triangle is equidistant from the extremities of the base.

16. If two isosceles triangles are on the same base, a line passing through their vertices is perpendicular to the base and bisects the base.

17. Two angles whose sides are perpendicular each to each are either equal or supplementary.

Under what circumstances are the angles equal, and under what circumstances are they supplementary?

156. The Analytic Method of Proof. The method of proof that asserts that a proposition under consideration is true if another proposition is true, and so on, step by step, until a known truth is reached, is called the *analytic method.*

This is the method resorted to when we do not see how to start the ordinary synthetic proof. The exercises on this page and on pages 81 and 82 may be investigated by the analytic method.

EXERCISE 17

1. The mid-point of the hypotenuse of a right triangle is equidistant from the three vertices.

Given M the mid-point of AC, the hypotenuse of the rt. $\triangle ABC$.

To prove that M is equidistant from A, B, and C.

We may reason thus: M is equidistant from A, B, and C if $AM = BM$. Why is this the case?

$AM = BM$ if the $\perp MN$ cuts $\triangle ABM$ into two congruent $\triangle$.

$\triangle ANM$ is congruent to $\triangle BNM$ if $AN = NB$.

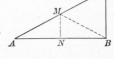

But AN does equal NB (§ 135), because MN is $\parallel$ to CB, and $AM = MC$.

Therefore the proposition is true.

We may now, in writing our proof, begin with this last step and work backwards, as in the synthetic proofs already considered.

2. If one acute angle of a right triangle is double the other, the hypotenuse is double the shorter side.

Given $\angle A = \angle a$, and $\angle C = \angle 2a$, to prove that AC is double BC. Let M be the mid-point of AC. Then AC is double BC if $AM = BC$. Why? Now if we draw $MN \parallel$ to CB, what can be said of the relation of AN and NB? Why? Then what may be said of $\triangle ANM$ and BNM? Why? Then what may be said of AM and BM? of $\angle a$ and $\angle q$? Therefore the proposition is

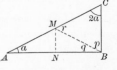

true if $BM = BC$. But $BM = BC$ if $\angle 2a = \angle r$, or if $\angle 2a = \angle a + \angle q$, or if $\angle a = \angle q$. But $\angle a = \angle q$ because we have proved that $AM = BM$.

Now reverse this reasoning and write the proof in the usual synthetic form.

3. A median of a triangle is less than half the sum of the two adjacent sides.

Given CM a median of the $\triangle ABC$.

To prove that $\quad CM < \frac{1}{2}(BC + CA)$.

Now $\qquad\qquad CM < \frac{1}{2}(BC + CA)$,

if $\qquad\qquad 2\,CM < BC + CA$.

This suggests producing CM by its own length to P, and drawing AP.

Then $\qquad\qquad\qquad CP = 2\,CM$,

and $\qquad 2\,CM < BC + CA$ if $CP < BC + CA$.

But $\qquad\qquad\qquad CP < AP + CA$. $\qquad\qquad$ Post. 3

$\qquad \therefore CP < BC + CA$ if $BC = AP$,

and $\qquad BC = AP$ if $\triangle MBC$ is congruent to $\triangle MAP$. $\qquad$ § 67

But $\qquad\qquad \triangle MBC$ is congruent to $\triangle MAP$, $\qquad\qquad$ § 68

for $\qquad\qquad\qquad MB = MA$, $\qquad\qquad\qquad\qquad$ Given

$\qquad\qquad\qquad CM = MP$, $\qquad\qquad\qquad\qquad$ Hyp.

and $\qquad\qquad \angle BMC = \angle AMP$. $\qquad\qquad\qquad$ § 60

$\qquad \therefore CP < BC + CA$.

$\qquad \therefore CM < \frac{1}{2}(BC + CA)$.

4. The line which bisects two sides of a triangle is parallel to the third side.

Given AD equal to DB, and AE equal to EC.

To prove that DE is ‖ to BC.

Suppose a line drawn from C ‖ to BA, and suppose DE produced to meet it at G.

$\qquad\qquad DE$ is ‖ to BC if $BCGD$ is a $\square$. $\qquad\qquad$ § 118

$\qquad\qquad BCGD$ is a $\square$ if $CG = BD$. $\qquad\qquad$ § 130

$\qquad\qquad CG = BD$ if each is equal to AD. $\qquad\qquad$ Ax. 8

Now $\qquad\qquad BD = AD$, $\qquad\qquad\qquad\qquad$ Given

and $\qquad CG = AD$ if $\triangle CGE$ is congruent to $\triangle ADE$. $\qquad$ § 67

But $\qquad\qquad \triangle CGE$ is congruent to $\triangle ADE$, $\qquad\qquad$ § 72

for $\qquad\qquad\qquad EC = AE$, $\qquad\qquad\qquad\qquad$ Given

$\qquad\qquad\qquad \angle CEG = \angle AED$, $\qquad\qquad\qquad$ § 60

and $\qquad\qquad \angle GCE = \angle A$. $\qquad\qquad\qquad\qquad$ § 100

5. Two isosceles triangles are congruent if a side and an angle of the one are equal respectively to the corresponding side and angle of the other.

The △ are congruent if what three corresponding parts are equal?

6. The bisector of an exterior angle of an isosceles triangle, formed by producing one of the equal sides through the vertex, is parallel to the base.

AE is ‖ to BC if what angles are equal? These angles are equal if $\angle CAD$ is twice what angle in the △?

7. If one of the equal sides of an isosceles triangle is produced through the vertex by its own length, the line joining the end of the side produced to the nearer end of the base is perpendicular to the base.

$\angle DBA$ is a rt. $\angle$ if it equals the sum of what △ of △ ABD? It equals this sum if $\angle p$ equals what angle and $\angle q$ equals what other angle?

8. If the equal sides of an isosceles triangle are produced through the vertex so that the external segments are equal, the extremities of these segments are equidistant from the extremities of the base respectively.

9. If the line drawn from the vertex of a triangle to the mid-point of the base is equal to half the base, the angle at the vertex is a right angle.

10. If through any point in the bisector of an angle a line is drawn parallel to either side of the angle, the triangle thus formed is isosceles.

11. Through any point C in the line AB an intersecting line is drawn, and from any two points in this line equidistant from C perpendiculars are drawn to AB or AB produced. Prove that these perpendiculars are equal.

12. The lines joining the mid-points of the sides of a triangle divide the triangle into four congruent triangles.

157. The Indirect Method of Proof. The method of proof that assumes the proposition false and then shows that this assumption is absurd is called the *indirect method* or the *reductio ad absurdum.*

This method forms a kind of last resort in the proof of a proposition, after the synthetic and analytic methods have failed.

EXERCISE 18

1. Given ABC and ABD, two triangles on the same base AB, and on the same side of it, the vertex of each triangle being outside the other triangle. Prove that if AC equals AD, then BC cannot equal BD.

Assume that $BC = BD$ and show that the result is absurd, since it would make D fall on C, which is contrary to the given conditions.

2. On the sides of the angle XOY two equal segments OA and OB are taken. On AB a triangle APB is constructed with AP greater than BP. Prove that OP cannot bisect the angle XOY.

Assume that OP does bisect $\angle XOY$. What is the result? Is this result possible?

3. From M, the mid-point of a line AB, MC is drawn oblique to AB. Prove that CA cannot equal CB.

Assume that CA does equal CB. What is the result? Is this result possible?

4. If perpendiculars are drawn to the sides of an acute angle from a point within the angle, they cannot inclose a right angle or an acute angle.

Assume that they inclose a right angle and show that this leads to an absurdity. Similarly for an acute angle.

5. One of the equal angles of an isosceles triangle is five ninths of a right angle. Prove that the angle at the vertex cannot be a right angle.

Assume that it is a right angle. Is the result possible?

158. General Suggestions for proving Theorems. The following general suggestions will often be helpful:

1. *Draw the figures as accurately as possible.*

This is especially helpful at first. A proof is often rendered difficult simply because the figure is carelessly drawn. If one line is to be laid off equal to another, or if one angle is to be made equal to another, do this by the help of the compasses or by measuring with a ruler.

2. *Draw as general figures as possible.*

If you wish to prove a proposition about a triangle, take a scalene triangle. If an equilateral triangle, for example, is taken, it may lead to believing something true for every kind of a triangle, when, in fact, it is true for only that particular kind.

3. *After drawing the figure state very clearly exactly what is given and exactly what is to be proved.*

Many of the difficulties of geometry come from failing to keep in mind *exactly* what is given and *exactly* what is to be proved.

4. *Then proceed synthetically with the proof if you see how to begin. If you do not see how to begin, try the analytic method, stating clearly that you could prove this if you could prove that, and so on until you reach a known proposition.*

5. *If two lines are to be proved equal, try to prove them corresponding sides of congruent triangles, or sides of an isosceles triangle, or opposite sides of a parallelogram, or segments between parallels that cut equal segments from another transversal.*

6. *If two angles are to be proved equal, try to prove them alternate-interior or exterior-interior angles of parallel lines, or corresponding angles of congruent triangles, or base angles of an isosceles triangle, or opposite angles of a parallelogram.*

7. *If one angle is to be proved greater than another, it is probably an exterior angle of a triangle, or an angle opposite the greater side of a triangle.*

8. *If one line is to be proved greater than another, it is probably opposite the greater angle of a triangle.*

EXERCISE 19

Prove the following propositions referring to equal lines:

1. If the sides AB and AD of a quadrilateral $ABCD$ are equal, and if the diagonal AC bisects the angle at A, then
BC is equal to DC.

2. A line is drawn terminated by two parallel lines. Through
its mid-point any line is drawn terminated by the parallels.
Prove that the second line is bisected by the first.

3. In a parallelogram $ABCD$ the line BQ
bisects AD, and DP bisects BC. Prove that
BQ and DP trisect AC.

4. On the base AB of a triangle ABC any
point P is taken. The lines AP, PB, BC, and
CA are bisected by W, X, Y, and Z respectively. Prove that XY is equal to WZ.

5. In an isosceles triangle the medians drawn to the equal
sides are equal.

6. In the square $ABCD$, CD is bisected by Q, and P and R
are taken on AB so that AP equals BR. Prove that PQ
equals RQ.

7. In this figure $AC = BC$, and $AP = BQ =$
$CR = CS$. Prove that $QR = PS$.

8. From the vertex and the mid-points of the equal sides of
an isosceles triangle lines are drawn perpendicular to the base.
Prove that they divide the base into four equal parts.

9. In the quadrilateral $ABCD$ it is known
that AB is parallel to DC, and that angle C
equals angle D. On CD two points are taken
such that $CP = DQ$. Prove that $AP = BQ$.

EXERCISE 20

Prove the following propositions referring to equal angles:

1. In this figure it is given that $AC=BC$, and that BQ and AR bisect the angles YBC and CAX respectively. Prove that $\triangle APB$ is isosceles.

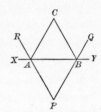

2. If through the vertices of an isosceles triangle lines are drawn parallel to the opposite sides, they form an isosceles triangle.

3. If the vertical angles of two isosceles triangles coincide, the bases either coincide or are parallel.

4. In which direction must the side of a triangle be produced so as to intersect the bisector of the opposite exterior angle?

Consider the cases, $\angle A < \angle C$, $\angle A = \angle C$, $\angle A > \angle C$.

5. The bisectors of the equal angles of an isosceles triangle form, together with the base, an isosceles triangle.

6. The bisectors of the base angles of an equilateral triangle form an angle equal to the exterior angle at the vertex of the triangle.

7. If the bisector of an exterior angle of a triangle is parallel to the opposite side, the triangle is isosceles.

8. A line drawn parallel to the base of an isosceles triangle makes equal angles with the sides or the sides produced.

9. A line drawn at right angles to AB, the base of an isosceles triangle ABC, cuts AC at P and BC produced at Q. Prove that PCQ is an isosceles triangle.

10. In this figure, if $AB = CD$, and $\angle A = \angle C$, then BD is parallel to AC.

EXERCISE 21

Prove the following propositions by showing that two triangles are congruent:

1. A perpendicular to the bisector of an angle forms with the sides an isosceles triangle.

2. If two lines bisect each other at right angles, any point in either is equidistant from the extremities of the other.

3. From B a perpendicular is drawn to the bisector of the angle A of the triangle ABC, meeting it at X, and meeting AC or AC produced at Y. Prove that $BX = XY$.

4. If through any point equally distant from two parallel lines two lines are drawn cutting the parallels, they intercept equal segments on these parallels.

5. If from the point where the bisector of an angle of a triangle meets the opposite side, parallels are drawn to the other two sides, and terminated by the sides, these parallels are equal.

6. The diagonals of a square are perpendicular to each other and bisect the angles of the square.

7. If from a vertex of a square there are drawn line-segments to the mid-points of the two sides not adjacent to the vertex, these line-segments are equal.

8. If either diagonal of a parallelogram bisects one of the angles, the sides of the parallelogram are all equal.

9. On the sides of any triangle ABC equilateral triangles BPC, CQA, ARB are constructed. Prove that $AP = BQ = CR$.

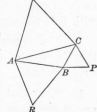

How can we prove that $\triangle ABP$ is congruent to $\triangle RBC$? Also that $\triangle ARC$ is congruent to $\triangle ABQ$? Does this prove the proposition?

EXERCISE 22

Prove the following propositions relating to the sum of the angles of a polygon :

1. An exterior angle of an acute triangle or of a right triangle cannot be acute.

2. If the sum of two angles of a triangle equals the third angle, the triangle is a right triangle.

3. If the line joining any vertex of a triangle to the midpoint of the opposite side divides the triangle into two isosceles triangles, the original triangle is a right triangle.

4. If the vertical angles of two isosceles triangles are supplements one of the other, the base angles of the one are complements of those of the other.

5. From the extremities of the base AB of a triangle ABC perpendiculars to the other two sides are drawn, meeting at P. Prove that the angle P is the supplement of the angle C.

6. If two sides of a quadrilateral are parallel, and the other two sides are equal but not parallel, the sums of the two pairs of opposite angles are equal.

7. The bisectors of two consecutive angles of a parallelogram are perpendicular to each other.

8. The exterior angles at B and C of any triangle ABC are bisected by lines meeting at P. Prove that the angle at P together with half the angle A equals a right angle.

9. The opposite angles of the quadrilateral formed by the bisectors of the interior angles of any quadrilateral are supplemental.

10. Show that Ex. 9 is true, if the bisectors of the exterior angles are taken.

EXERCISE 23

Prove the following propositions referring to greater lines or greater angles:

1. In the triangle ABC the angle A is bisected by a line meeting BC at D. Prove that BA is greater than BD, and CA greater than CD.

2. In the quadrilateral $ABCD$ it is known that AD is the longest side and BC the shortest side. Prove that the angle B is greater than the angle D, and the angle C greater than the angle A.

3. A line is drawn from the vertex A of a square $ABCD$ so as to cut CD and to meet BC produced in P. Prove that AP is greater than DB.

4. If the angle between two adjacent sides of a parallelogram is increased, the length of the sides remaining unchanged, the diagonal from the vertex of this angle is diminished.

5. Within a triangle ABC a point P is taken such that $CP = CB$. Prove that AB is always greater than AP.

6. In a quadrilateral $ABCD$ it is known that AD equals BC and that the angle C is less than the angle D. Prove that the diagonal AC is greater than the diagonal BD.

7. In the quadrilateral $ABCD$ it is known that AD equals BC and that the angle D is greater than the angle C. Prove that the angle B is greater than the angle A.

8. In the triangle ABC the side AB is greater than AC. On AB and AC respectively BP is taken equal to CQ. Prove that BQ is greater than CP.

9. The sum of the distances of any point from the three vertices of a triangle is greater than half the sum of the sides.

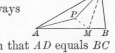

Prove the following miscellaneous exercises :

1. The line joining the mid-points of the nonparallel sides of a trapezoid passes through the mid-points of the two diagonals.

How is *EF* related to *AB* and *DC* ? Why ?
Since *EF* bisects *BC* and *AD*, how does it divide *AC* and *BD* ? Why ?

2. The lines joining the mid-points of the consecutive sides of any quadrilateral form a parallelogram.

How are *PQ* and *SR* related to *AC* ?

3. If the diagonals of a trapezoid are equal, the trapezoid is isosceles.

Draw *CE* and *DF* ⊥ to *AB*.
How is △ *ADF* related to △ *BCE* ? Why ?
Then how is ∠ *FAD* related to ∠ *CBA* ?
Then how is △ *ABC* related to △ *BAD* ? Why ?

4. If from the diagonal *DB*, of a square *ABCD*, *BE* is cut off equal to *BC*, and *EF* is drawn perpendicular to *BD*, meeting *DC* at *F*, then *DE* is equal to *EF* and also to *FC*.

How many degrees in ∡ *EDF* and *DFE* ? How is *DE* related to *EF* ? Why ?
Then how is rt. △ *BEF* related to rt. △ *BCF* ? Why ?

5. If the opposite sides of a hexagon are equal and parallel, the diagonals that join opposite vertices meet in a point.

6. If perpendiculars are drawn from the four vertices of a parallelogram to any line outside the parallelogram, the sum of the perpendiculars from one pair of opposite vertices equals the sum of those from the other pair.

How are *x* + *y* and *w* + *z* related to *k* ?

EXERCISE 25

Examination Questions

1. The sum of the four sides of any quadrilateral is greater than the sum of the diagonals.

2. The lines joining the mid-points of the sides of a square, taken in order, form a square.

3. In a quadrilateral the angle between the bisectors of two consecutive angles is one half the sum of the other two angles.

4. If the opposite sides of a hexagon are equal, does it follow that they are parallel? Give reasons for your answer.

5. In a triangle ABC the side BC is bisected at P and AB is bisected at Q. AP is produced to R so that $AP = PR$, and CQ is produced to S so that $CQ = QS$. Prove that S, B, and R are in a straight line.

6. If the diagonals of a parallelogram are equal, all of the angles of the parallelogram are equal.

7. In the triangle ABC, $\angle A = 60°$ and $\angle B > \angle C$. Which is the longest and which is the shortest side of the triangle? Prove it.

8. How many sides has a polygon each of whose interior angles is equal to 175°?

9. Given the quadrilateral $ABCD$, with AB equal to AD, and BC equal to CD. Prove that the diagonal AC bisects the angle DCB and is perpendicular to the diagonal BD.

10. In how many ways can two congruent triangles be put together to form a parallelogram? Draw the diagrams.

11. The sides of a polygon of an odd number of sides are produced to meet, thus forming a star-shaped figure. What is the sum of the angles at the points of the star?

The propositions in Exercise 25 are taken from recent college entrance examination papers.

EXERCISE 26

Review Questions

1. Define and illustrate rectilinear and curvilinear figures.

2. Upon what does the size of an angle depend?

3. What is meant by the bisector of a magnitude? Illustrate when the magnitude is a line; an angle.

4. Define perpendicular and state three facts relating to a perpendicular to a line.

5. Name and define the parts of a triangle and such special lines connected with a triangle as you have thus far studied.

6. Classify angles.

7. Classify triangles as to angles; as to sides.

8. Define and illustrate complementary, supplementary, and conjugate angles.

9. What are the two classes of assumptions in geometry? Give the list of each.

10. State all of the conditions of congruency of two triangles.

11. What is meant by the converse of a proposition?

12. Are two triangles always congruent if three parts of the one are respectively equal to three parts of the other?

13. State three tests for determining whether one line is parallel to another.

14. State the proposition relating to the sum of the angles of a triangle, and state a proposition that can be proved by its use.

15. State a proposition relating to two unequal angles of a triangle; to two unequal sides of a triangle.

16. Must a triangle be equiangular if equilateral? Must a triangle be equilateral if equiangular?

17. Classify polygons as to sides; as to angles.

18. Define locus and give three illustrations.

BOOK II

THE CIRCLE

159. Circle. A closed curve lying in a plane, and such that all of its points are equally distant from a fixed point in the plane, is called a *circle*.

160. Circle as a Locus. It follows that *the locus of a point in a plane at a given distance from a fixed point is a circle.*

161. Radius. A straight line from the center to the circle is called a *radius*.

162. Equal Radii. It follows that *all radii of the same circle or of equal circles are equal*, and that *all circles of equal radii are equal.*

163. Diameter. A straight line through the center, terminated at each end by the circle, is called a *diameter*.

Since a diameter equals two radii, it follows that *all diameters of the same circle or of equal circles are equal.*

164. Arc. Any portion of a circle is called an *arc*.

An arc that is half of a circle is called a *semicircle*.

An arc less than a semicircle is called a *minor arc*, and an arc greater than a semicircle is called a *major arc*. The word *arc* taken alone is generally understood to mean a minor arc.

165. Central Angle. If the vertex of an angle is at the center of a circle and the sides are radii of the circle, the angle is called a *central angle*.

An angle is said to *intercept* any arc cut off by its sides, and the arc is said to *subtend* the angle.

Proposition I. Theorem

166. *In the same circle or in equal circles equal central angles intercept equal arcs; and of two unequal central angles the greater intercepts the greater arc.*

Given two equal circles with centers *O* and *O'*, with angles *AOB* and *A'O'B'* equal, and with angle *AOC* greater than angle *A'O'B'*.

To prove that   1. arc *AB* = arc *A'B'*;

                       2. arc *AC* > arc *A'B'*.

Proof. 1. Place the circle with center *O* on the circle with center *O'* so that ∠ *AOB* shall coincide with its equal, ∠ *A'O'B'*. In the case of the same circle, swing one angle about *O* until it coincides with its equal angle.   Post. 5

           Then *A* falls on *A'*, and *B* on *B'*.   § 162

              (Radii of equal circles are equal.)

      ∴ arc *AB* coincides with arc *A'B'*.   § 159

    (Every point of each is equally distant from the center.)

Proof. 2. Since ∠ *AOC* is greater than ∠ *A'O'B'*,   Given

and   ∠ *AOB* = ∠ *A'O'B'*,   Given

therefore   ∠ *AOC* is greater than ∠ *AOB*.   Ax. 9

         Therefore *OC* lies outside ∠ *AOB*.

                ∴ arc *AC* > arc *AB*.   Ax. 11

But   arc *AB* = arc *A'B'*.

        ∴ arc *AC* > arc *A'B'*, by Ax. 9.   Q. E. D.

Proposition II. Theorem

167. *In the same circle or in equal circles equal arcs subtend equal central angles; and of two unequal arcs the greater subtends the greater central angle.*

Given two equal circles with centers O and O', with arcs AB and $A'B'$ equal, and with arc AC greater than arc $A'B'$.

To prove that
    1. $\angle AOB = \angle A'O'B'$;
    2. $\angle AOC > \angle A'O'B'$.

Proof. 1. Using the figure of Prop. I, place the circle with center O on the circle with center O' so that OA shall fall on its equal $O'A'$, and the arc AB on its equal $A'B'$.   Post. 5

    Then OB coincides with $O'B'$.   Post. 1

    $\therefore \angle AOB = \angle A'O'B'$.   § 23

Proof. 2. Since arc $AC >$ arc $A'B'$, it is greater than arc AB, the equal of arc $A'B'$, and OB lies within the $\angle AOC$.   Ax. 9

    $\therefore \angle AOC > \angle AOB$.   Ax. 11

    $\therefore \angle AOC > \angle A'O'B'$, by Ax. 9.   Q.E.D.

This proposition is the converse of Prop. I.

168. Law of Converse Theorems. Of four magnitudes, a, b, x, y, if
    (1) $a > b$ when $x > y$,
    (2) $a = b$ when $x = y$,
and   (3) $a < b$ when $x < y$,
then *the converses of these three statements are always true.*

For when $a > b$ it is impossible that $x = y$, for then a would equal b by (2); or that $x < y$, for then a would be less than b by (3). Hence $x > y$ when $a > b$. In the same way, $x = y$ when $a = b$, and $x < y$ when $a < b$.

169. Chord. A straight line that has its extremities on a circle is called a *chord*.

A chord is said to *subtend* the arcs that it cuts from a circle. Unless the contrary is stated, the chord is taken as subtending the minor arc.

Proposition III. Theorem

170. *In the same circle or in equal circles, if two arcs are equal, they are subtended by equal chords; and if two arcs are unequal, the greater is subtended by the greater chord.*

Given two equal circles with centers *O* and *O'*, with arcs *AB* and *A'B'* equal, and with arc *AF* greater than arc *A'B'*.

To prove that　　1.　*chord AB = chord A'B' ;*

　　　　　　　　　2.　*chord AF > chord A'B'.*

Proof. 1. Draw the radii *OA, OB, OF, O'A', O'B'.*

Since　　　　　　　*OA = O'A',* and *OB = O'B',*　　　　　§ 162

and　　　　　　　　∠ *AOB = ∠ A'O'B',*　　　　　　　§ 167

　　　　　　(In equal ⊚ equal arcs subtend equal central ∡.)

　　　　∴ △ *OAB* is congruent to △ *O'A'B',*　　　　§ 68

and　　　　　　　chord *AB =* chord *A'B'.*　　　　　§ 67

Proof. 2. In the △ *OAF* and *O'A'B',*

　　　　　　　OA = O'A', and *OF = O'B',*　　　　　§ 162

but　　　　　　∠ *AOF* is greater than ∠ *A'O'B'.*　　§ 167

(In equal ⊚, of two unequal arcs the greater subtends the greater central ∠.)

　　　　∴ chord *AF >* chord *A'B',* by § 115.　　　　Q.E.D.

171. Corollary. *In the same circle or in equal circles, the greater of two unequal major arcs is subtended by the less chord.*

PROPOSITION IV. THEOREM

172. *In the same circle or in equal circles, if two chords are equal, they subtend equal arcs ; and if two chords are unequal, the greater subtends the greater arc.*

 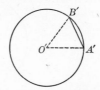

Given two equal circles with centers O and O', with chords AB and $A'B'$ equal, and with chord AF greater than chord $A'B'$.

To prove that   1. arc AB = arc $A'B'$;

                  2. arc AF > arc $A'B'$.

Proof. 1. Draw the radii OA, OB, OF, $O'A'$, $O'B'$.

Since	$OA = O'A'$, and $OB = O'B'$,	§ 162
and	chord AB = chord $A'B'$,	Given
	∴ △ OAB is congruent to △ $O'A'B'$,	§ 80
and	∠ AOB = ∠ $A'O'B'$.	§ 67
	∴ arc AB = arc $A'B'$.	§ 166

Proof. 2. In the △△ OAF and $O'A'B'$,

	$OA = O'A'$, and $OF = O'B'$,	§ 162
but	chord AF > chord $A'B'$.	Given
	∴ ∠ AOF > ∠ $A'O'B'$.	§ 116
	∴ arc AF > arc $A'B'$, by § 166.	Q.E.D.

This proposition is the converse of Prop. III.

173. COROLLARY. *In the same circle or in equal circles the greater of two unequal chords subtends the less major arc.*

PROPOSITION V. THEOREM

174. *A line through the center of a circle perpendicular to a chord bisects the chord and the arcs subtended by it.*

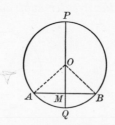

Given the line *PQ* through the center *O* of the circle *AQBP*, perpendicular to the chord *AB* at *M*.

To prove that AM = BM, arc AQ = arc BQ, and arc AP = arc BP.

Proof.   Draw the radii *OA* and *OB*.

Then since $OM = OM$,   Iden.

and $OA = OB$,   § 162

∴ rt. △ *AMO* is congruent to rt. △ *BMO*.   § 89

∴ $AM = BM$, and $\angle AOQ = \angle QOB$.   § 67

Likewise $\angle POA = \angle BOP$.   § 58

∴ arc AQ = arc BQ, and arc AP = arc BP, by § 166.   Q. E. D.

175. COROLLARY 1. *A diameter bisects the circle.*

176. COROLLARY 2. *A line through the center that bisects a chord is perpendicular to the chord.*

177. COROLLARY 3. *The perpendicular bisector of a chord passes through the center of the circle and bisects the arcs subtended by the chord.*

How many bisectors of the chord are possible ? How many ⊥ bisectors ? Therefore with what line must this coincide (§ 174) ?

Proposition VI. Theorem

178. *In the same circle or in equal circles equal chords are equidistant from the center, and chords equidistant from the center are equal.*

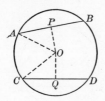

Given *AB* and *CD*, equal chords of the circle *ACDB*.

To prove that AB and CD are equidistant from the center O.

Proof.   Draw $OP \perp$ to AB, and $OQ \perp$ to CD.

Draw the radii *OA* and *OC*.

OP bisects *AB*, and *OQ* bisects *CD*.		§ 174

Then since $AP = CQ$,   Ax. 4

and $OA = OC$,   § 162

$\therefore$ rt. $\triangle OPA$ is congruent to rt. $\triangle OQC$.   § 89

$\therefore OP = OQ$.   § 67

$\therefore$ *AB* and *CD* are equidistant from *O*, by § 88.   **Q.E.D.**

Given *OP* and *OQ*, equal perpendiculars from the center *O* to the chords *AB* and *CD*.

To prove that $AB = CD$.

Proof. Since $OA = OC$,   § 162

and $OP = OQ$,   Given

$\therefore$ rt. $\triangle OPA$ is congruent to rt. $\triangle OQC$.   § 89

$\therefore AP = CQ$.   § 67

$\therefore AB = CD$, by **Ax. 3**.   **Q.E.D.**

Proposition VII. Theorem

179. *In the same circle or in equal circles, if two chords are unequal, they are unequally distant from the center, and the greater chord is at the less distance.*

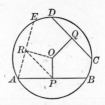

Given a circle with center O, two unequal chords AB and CD, AB being the greater, and OP perpendicular to AB, and OQ perpendicular to CD.

To prove that $\qquad OP < OQ$.

Proof. Suppose AE drawn equal to CD, and $OR \perp$ to AE.

$\qquad\qquad$ Draw PR.

$\qquad OP$ bisects AB, and OR bisects AE. $\qquad\qquad$ § 174

(A line through the center of a circle ⊥ to a chord bisects the chord.)

$\qquad\qquad$ But $AB > CD$. $\qquad\qquad\qquad\qquad$ Given

$\qquad \therefore AB > AE$, the equal of CD. $\qquad\qquad$ Ax. 9

$\qquad\qquad \therefore AP > AR.$ $\qquad\qquad\qquad\qquad$ Ax. 6

$\qquad\qquad \therefore \angle ARP > \angle RPA.$ $\qquad\qquad\qquad$ § 113

(If two sides of a △ are unequal, the ⩦ opposite these sides are unequal, and the ∠ opposite the greater side is the greater.)

$\therefore \angle PRO$, the complement of $\angle ARP$, is less than $\angle OPR$, the complement of $\angle RPA$. $\qquad\qquad\qquad\qquad$ § 59

$\qquad\qquad\qquad \therefore OP < OR.$ $\qquad\qquad\qquad$ § 114

But $\qquad\qquad\qquad\quad OR = OQ.$ $\qquad\qquad\qquad$ § 178

$\qquad\qquad \therefore OP < OQ$, by **Ax. 9.** $\qquad\qquad$ Q.E.D.

Proposition VIII. Theorem

180. *In the same circle or in equal circles, if two chords are unequally distant from the center, they are unequal, and the chord at the less distance is the greater.*

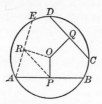

Given a circle with center *O*, two chords *AB* and *CD* unequally distant from *O*, and *OP*, the perpendicular to *AB*, less than *OQ*, the perpendicular to *CD*.

To prove that $AB > CD$.

Proof. Suppose *AE* drawn equal to *CD*, and *OR* ⊥ to *AE*.

Now	$OP < OQ$,	Given
and	$OR = OQ$.	§ 178
	$\therefore OP < OR$.	Ax. 9
Drawing *PR*,	$\angle PRO < \angle OPR$.	§ 113

$\therefore \angle ARP$, the complement of $\angle PRO$, is greater than $\angle RPA$, the complement of $\angle OPR$.   § 59

	$\therefore AP > AR$.	§ 114
But	$AP = \frac{1}{2}AB$, and $AR = \frac{1}{2}AE$.	§ 174
	$\therefore AB > AE$.	Ax. 6
But	$CD = AE$.	Hyp.
	$\therefore AB > CD$, by Ax. 9.	Q.E.D.

This proposition is the converse of Prop. VII.

181. Corollary. *A diameter of a circle is greater than any other chord.*

182. Secant. A straight line that intersects a circle is called a *secant*. In this figure AD is a secant.

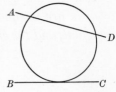

Since only two equal obliques can be drawn to a line from an external point (§ 85), and since the two equal angles which radii make (§ 74) with any secant where it cuts the circle cannot be right angles (§ 109), they must be oblique; and hence it follows that *a secant can intersect the circle in only two points.*

183. Tangent. A straight line of unlimited length that has one point, and only one, in common with a circle is called a *tangent* to the circle.

In this case the circle is said to be tangent to the line. Thus in the figure, BC is tangent to the circle, and the circle is tangent to BC.

The common point is called the *point of contact* or *point of tangency*.

By the tangent from an external point to a circle is meant the line-segment from the external point to the point of contact.

EXERCISE 27

1. A radius that bisects an arc bisects its subtending chord and is perpendicular to it.

2. On a circle the point P is equidistant from two radii OA and OB. Prove that P bisects the arc AB.

3. In this circle the chords AM and MB are equal. Prove that M bisects the arc AB and that the radius OM bisects the chord AB.

4. On a circle are five points, A, B, C, D, E, so placed that AB, BC, CD, DE are equal chords. Prove that AC, BD, CE are equal chords, and that AD and BE are also equal chords.

5. If two chords intersect and make equal angles with the diameter through their point of intersection, these chords are equal.

Proposition IX. Theorem

184. *A line perpendicular to a radius at its extremity is tangent to the circle.*

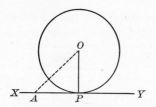

Given a circle, with *XY* perpendicular to the radius *OP* at *P*.

To prove that XY is tangent to the circle.

Proof. From *O* draw any other line to *XY*, as *OA*.

Then $OA > OP$.   § 86

∴ the point *A* is outside the circle.   § 160

Hence every point, except *P*, of the line *XY* is outside the circle.

Therefore *XY* is tangent to the circle at *P*, by § 183.   Q.E.D.

185. Corollary 1. *A tangent to a circle is perpendicular to the radius drawn to the point of contact.*

For *OP* is the shortest line from *O* to *XY*, and is therefore ⊥ to *XY* (§ 86) ; that is, *XY* is ⊥ to *OP*.

186. Corollary 2. *A perpendicular to a tangent at the point of contact passes through the center of the circle.*

For a radius is ⊥ to a tangent at the point of contact, and therefore a ⊥ erected at the point of contact coincides with this radius and passes through the center of the circle.

187. Corollary 3. *A perpendicular from the center of a circle to a tangent passes through the point of contact.*

What does § 86 say about this perpendicular ?

188. Concentric Circles. Two circles that have the same center are said to be *concentric*.

EXERCISE 28

1. The shortest chord that can be drawn through a given point within a circle is that which is perpendicular to the diameter through the point.

Show that any other chord, *CD*, through *P*, is nearer *O* than is *AB*.

2. The diameter *CD* bisects the arc *AB*. Prove that $\angle CBA = \angle BAC$.

What kind of a triangle is $\triangle ABC$?

3. Tangents at the extremities of a diameter are parallel.

4. The arc *AB* is greater than the arc *BC*. *OP* and *OQ* are perpendiculars from the center to *AB* and *BC* respectively. Prove that $\angle QPO$ is greater than $\angle OQP$.

5. What is the locus of the center of a circle tangent to the line *XY* at the point *P*? Prove it.

What two conditions must be shown to be fulfilled?

6. What is the locus of the mid-points of a number of parallel chords of a circle? Prove it.

7. Three equal chords, *AB*, *BC*, *CD*, are placed end to end, and the radii *OA*, *OB*, *OC*, *OD* are drawn. Prove that $\angle AOC = \angle BOD$.

8. All equal chords of a circle are tangent to a concentric circle.

9. If a number of equal chords are drawn in this circle, the figure gives the impression of a second circle inside the first and concentric with it. Explain the reason.

Proposition X. Theorem

189. *Two parallel lines intercept equal arcs on a circle.*

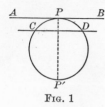 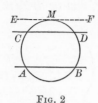 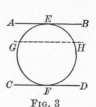

Fig. 1 Fig. 2 Fig. 3

CASE 1. *When the parallels are a tangent and a secant* (Fig. 1).

Given *AB*, a tangent at *P*, parallel to *CD*, a secant.

To prove that arc *CP* = arc *DP*.

Proof. Suppose *PP'* drawn ⊥ to *AB* at *P*.

Then *PP'* is a diameter of the circle. § 186

And *PP'* is also ⊥ to *CD*. § 97

∴ arc *CP* = arc *DP*. § 174

CASE 2. *When the parallels are both secants* (Fig. 2).

Given *AB* and *CD*, parallel secants.

To prove that arc *AC* = arc *BD*.

Proof. Suppose *EF* ∥ to *CD* and tangent to the circle at *M*.

Then arc *AM* = arc *BM*, and arc *CM* = arc *DM*. Case 1

∴ arc *AC* = arc *BD*. Ax. 2

CASE 3. *When the parallels are both tangents* (Fig. 3).

Given *AB*, a tangent at *E*, parallel to *CD*, a tangent at *F*.

To prove that arc *FGE* = arc *FHE*.

Proof. Suppose a secant *GH* drawn ∥ to *AB*.

Then arc *GE* = arc *HE*, and arc *FG* = arc *FH*. Case 1

∴ arc *FGE* = arc *FHE*, by Ax. 1. Q. E. D.

Proposition XI. Theorem

190. *Through three points not in a straight line one circle, and only one, can be drawn.*

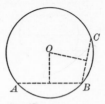

Given *A*, *B*, *C*, three points not in a straight line.

To prove that one circle, and only one, can be drawn through A, B, and C.

Proof.   Draw *AB* and *BC*.

At the mid-points of *AB* and *BC* suppose ⊥s erected.

These ⊥s will intersect at some point *O*, since *AB* and *BC* are neither parallel nor in the same straight line.

The point *O* is in the perpendicular bisector of *AB*, and is therefore equidistant from *A* and *B*; the point *O* is also in the perpendicular bisector of *BC*, and is therefore equidistant from *B* and *C*.   § 150

Therefore *O* is equidistant from *A*, *B*, and *C*.

Therefore a circle described about *O* as a center, with a radius *OA*, will pass through the three given points.   § 160

The center of any circle that passes through the three points must be in both of these perpendicular bisectors, and hence at their intersection. As two straight lines can intersect in only one point (§ 55), *O* is the only point that can be the center of a circle through the three given points.   Q. E. D.

191. Corollary. *Two circles can intersect in only two points.*

If two circles have three points in common, can it be shown that they coincide and form one circle?

Proposition XII. Theorem

192. *The tangents to a circle drawn from an external point are equal, and make equal angles with the line joining the point to the center.*

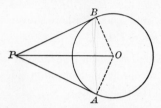

Given *PA* and *PB*, tangents from *P* to the circle whose center is *O*, and *PO* the line joining *P* to the center *O*.

To prove that $PA = PB$, and $\angle APO = \angle OPB$.

Proof. Draw *OA* and *OB*.

PA is $\perp$ to *OA*, and *PB* is $\perp$ to *OB*. § 185

(*A tangent to a circle is $\perp$ to the radius drawn to the point of contact.*)

In the rt. $\triangle$ *PAO* and *PBO*,

$$PO = PO,$$ Iden.

and $$OA = OB.$$ § 162

$\therefore$ rt. $\triangle$ *PAO* is congruent to rt. $\triangle$ *PBO*. § 89

$\therefore PA = PB$, and $\angle APO = \angle OPB$, by § 67. Q.E.D.

193. Line of Centers. The line determined by the centers of two circles is called the *line of centers.*

194. Tangent Circles. Two circles that are both tangent to the same line at the same point are called *tangent circles.*

Circles are said to be tangent *internally* or *externally*, according as they lie on the same side of the tangent line or on opposite sides. E.g. the two circles shown in the figure on page 110 are tangent externally.

The point of contact with the line is called the *point of contact* or *point of tangency* of the circles.

EXERCISE 29

1. Show that the reasoning of § 190 will not hold for four points, and hence that a circle cannot always be drawn through four points.

2. Tangents to a circle at A, B, C, points on the circle, meet in P and Q, as here shown. Prove that $AP + QC = PQ$.

3. If a quadrilateral has each side tangent to a circle, the sum of one pair of opposite sides equals the sum of the other pair.

In this figure, $SP + QR = PQ + RS$.

4. The hexagon here shown has each side tangent to the circle. Prove that $AB + CD + EF = BC + DE + FA$.

5. In this figure CF is a diameter perpendicular to the parallel chords DB and EA, and arc $AB = 40°$ and arc $BC = 50°$. How many degrees are there in arcs CD, DE, EF, and FA?

6. In this figure XY is tangent to the circle at B, the chord CA is perpendicular to the diameter BD, and the arc $CD = 150°$. How many degrees are there in arc AB?

7. If a quadrilateral has each side tangent to a circle, the sum of the angles at the center subtended by any two opposite sides is equal to a straight angle.

8. AP and CQ are parallel tangents meeting a third tangent QP, as shown in the figure. O being the center, prove that the angle POQ is a right angle.

Are A, O, and C in the same straight line? Draw OA and OC, and find the relations of the $\angle$s at O to those at P and Q.

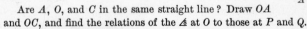

Proposition XIII. Theorem

195. *If two circles intersect, the line of centers is the perpendicular bisector of their common chord.*

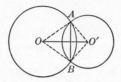

Given O and O', the centers of two intersecting circles, AB the common chord, and OO' the line of centers.

To prove that OO' is $\perp$ to AB at its mid-point.

Proof.   Draw OA, OB, $O'A$, and $O'B$.

$$OA = OB, \text{ and } O'A = O'B. \qquad \S\ 162$$

∴ O and O' are two points, each equidistant from A and B.

∴ OO' is the perpendicular bisector of AB, by § 151.   q.e.d.

196. Common Tangents. A tangent to two circles is called a *common external tangent* if it does not cut the line-segment joining the centers, and a *common internal tangent* if it cuts it.

EXERCISE 30

Describe the relative position of two circles if the line-segment joining the centers is related to the radii as stated in Exs. 1–5, and illustrate each case by a figure:

1. The line-segment greater than the sum of the radii.

2. The line-segment equal to the sum of the radii.

3. The line-segment less than the sum but greater than the difference of the radii.

4. The line-segment equal to the difference of the radii.

5. The line-segment less than the difference of the radii.

Proposition XIV. Theorem

197. *If two circles are tangent to each other, the line of centers passes through the point of contact.*

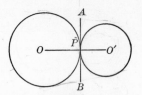

Given two circles tangent at *P*.

To prove that P is in the line of centers.

Proof. Let *AB* be the common tangent at *P*.   § 194

Then a ⊥ to *AB*, drawn through the point *P*, passes through the centers *O* and *O'*.   § 186

(*A ⊥ to a tangent at the point of contact passes through the center of the circle.*)

Therefore the line determined by *O* and *O'*, having two points in common with this ⊥, must coincide with it.   Post. 1

∴ *P* is in the line of centers.   Q.E.D.

EXERCISE 31

Describe the relative position of two circles having tangents as stated in Exs. 1–5, and illustrate each case by a figure:

1. Two common external and two common internal tangents.

2. Two common external tangents and one common internal tangent.

3. Two common external tangents and no common internal tangent.

4. One common external and no common internal tangent.

5. No common tangent.

6. The line which passes through the mid-points of two parallel chords passes through the center of the circle.

7. If two circles are tangent externally, the tangents to them from any point of the common internal tangent are equal.

8. If two circles tangent externally are tangent to a line AB at A and B, their common internal tangent bisects AB.

9. The line drawn from the center of a circle to the point of intersection of two tangents is the perpendicular bisector of the chord joining the points of contact.

10. The diameters of two circles are respectively 2.74 in. and 3.48 in. Find the distance between the centers of the circles if they are tangent externally. Find the distance between the centers of the circles if they are tangent internally.

11. Three circles of diameters 4.8 in., 3.6 in., and 4.2 in. are externally tangent, each to the other two. Find the perimeter of the triangle formed by joining the centers.

12. A circle of center O and radius r' rolls around a fixed circle of radius r. What is the locus of O? Prove it.

13. The line drawn from the mid-point of a chord to the mid-point of its subtended arc is perpendicular to the chord.

— 14. If two circles tangent externally at P are tangent to a line AB at A and B, the angle BPA is a right angle.

— 15. Three circles are tangent externally at the points A, B, and C, and the chords AB and AC are produced to cut the circle BC at D and E. Prove that DE is a diameter.

—16. If two radii of a circle, at right angles to each other, when produced are cut by a tangent to the circle at A and B, the other tangents from A and B are parallel to each other.

17. If two common external tangents or two common internal tangents are drawn to two circles, the line-segments intercepted between the points of contact are equal.

198. Measure. The number of times a quantity of any kind contains a known unit of the same kind, expressed in terms of that known unit, is called the *measure* of the quantity.

Thus we measure the *length* of a schoolroom by finding the number of times it contains a *known unit* called the *foot*. We measure the *area* of the floor by finding the number of times it contains a *known unit* called the *square foot*. You measure your weight by finding the number of times it contains a *known unit* called the *pound*. Thus the measure of the length of a room may be 30 ft., the measure of the area of the floor may be 600 sq. ft., and so on.

The abstract number found in measuring a quantity is called its *numerical measure,* or usually simply its *measure.*

199. Ratio. The quotient of the numerical measures of two quantities, expressed in terms of a common unit, is called the *ratio* of the quantities.

Thus, if a room is 20 ft. by 35 ft., the ratio of the width to the length is 20 ft. $\div$ 35 ft., or $\frac{20}{35}$, which reduces to $\frac{4}{7}$. Here the *common unit* is 1 ft.

The ratio of a to b is written $\frac{a}{b}$, or $a : b$, as in arithmetic and algebra.

Thus the ratio of 20° to 30° is $\frac{20}{30}$, or $\frac{2}{3}$, or 2 : 3.

200. Commensurable Magnitudes. Two quantities of the same kind that can both be expressed in integers in terms of a common unit are said to be *commensurable magnitudes.*

Thus 20 ft. and 35 ft. are expressed in integers (20 and 35) in terms of a common unit (1 ft.); similarly 2 ft and $3\frac{1}{2}$ ft., the integers being 4 and 7, and the common unit being $\frac{1}{2}$ ft.

The common unit used in measuring two or more commensurable magnitudes is called their *common measure.* Each of the magnitudes is called a *multiple* of this common measure.

201. Incommensurable Magnitudes. Two quantities of the same kind that cannot both be expressed in integers in terms of a common unit are said to be *incommensurable magnitudes.*

Thus, if $a = \sqrt{2}$ and $b = 3$, there is no number that is contained an integral number of times in both $\sqrt{2}$ and 3. Hence a and b are, in this case, incommensurable magnitudes.

202. Incommensurable Ratio. The ratio of two incommensurable magnitudes is called an *incommensurable ratio*.

Although the exact value of such a ratio cannot be expressed by an integer, a common fraction, or a decimal fraction of a limited number of places, it may be expressed *approximately*.

Thus suppose $\dfrac{a}{b} = \sqrt{2}$.

Now $\sqrt{2} = 1.41421356\cdots$, which is greater than 1.414213 but less than 1.414214. Then if a *millionth part* of b is taken as the unit of measure, the value of $a : b$ lies between 1.414213 and 1.414214, and therefore differs from either by less than 0.000001.

By carrying the decimal further an approximate value may be found that will differ from the ratio by less than a *billionth*, a *trillionth*, or *any other assigned value*.

That is, *for practical purposes all ratios are commensurable.*

For example, if $\dfrac{a}{b} > \dfrac{m}{n}$ but $< \dfrac{m+1}{n}$, then the error in taking either of these values for $\dfrac{a}{b}$ is less than $\dfrac{1}{n}$, the difference of these ratios. But by increasing n indefinitely, $\dfrac{1}{n}$ can be decreased indefinitely, and a value of the ratio can be found within any required degree of accuracy.

EXERCISE 32

Find a common measure of :

1. 32 in., 24 in.	**3.** $5\frac{1}{2}$ in., $3\frac{1}{2}$ in.	**5.** $6\frac{1}{3}$ da., $2\frac{2}{3}$ da.
2. 48 ft., 18 ft.	**4.** $2\frac{3}{4}$ lb., $1\frac{1}{2}$ lb.	**6.** 14.4 in., 1.2 in.

Find the greatest common measure of :

7. 64 yd., 24 yd.	**9.** 7.5 in., 1.25 in.	**11.** $2\frac{3}{4}$ ft., 0.25 ft.
8. 51 ft., 17 ft.	**10.** $3\frac{1}{3}$ in., $0.33\frac{1}{3}$ in.	**12.** 75°, 7° 30′.

13. If $a : b = \sqrt{3}$, find an approximate value of this ratio that shall differ from the true value by less than 0.001.

203. Constant and Variable. A quantity regarded as having a fixed value throughout a given discussion is called a *constant*, but a quantity regarded as having different successive values is called a *variable*.

204. Limit. When a variable approaches a constant in such a way that the difference between the two may become and remain less than any assigned positive quantity, however small, the constant is called the *limit* of the variable.

Variables can sometimes reach their limits and sometimes not. E.g. a chord may increase in length up to a certain limit, the diameter, and it can reach this limit and still be a chord ; it may decrease, approaching the limit 0, but it cannot reach this limit and still be a chord.

205. Inscribed and Circumscribed Polygons. If the sides of a polygon are all chords of a circle, the polygon is said to be *inscribed* in the circle ; if the sides are all tangents to a circle, the polygon is said to be *circum-scribed* about the circle.

The circle is said to be *circum-scribed* about the inscribed polygon, and to be *inscribed* in the circum-scribed polygon.

Inscribed   Circumscribed
Polygon   Polygon

206. Circle as a Limit. If we inscribe a square in a circle, and then inscribe an octagon by taking the mid-points of the four equal arcs for the new vertices, the octa-gon is greater than the square but smaller than the area inclosed by the circle, and the perim-eter of the octagon is greater than the perim-eter of the square (§ 112).

By continually doubling the number of sides in this way it appears that the area inclosed by the circle is the limit of the area of the polygon, and the circle is the limit of its perimeter, as the number of sides is indefinitely increased.

Hence we have limiting *forms* as well as limiting *values*, the form of the circle being the limit approached by the form of the inscribed polygon.

207. Principle of Limits. *If, while approaching their respective limits, two variables are always equal, their limits are equal.*

Let AX and BY increase in length in such a way that they always remain equal, and let their respective limits be AL and BM.

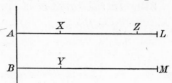

To prove that $AL = BM$.

Suppose these limits are not equal, but that $AZ = BM$.

Then since X may reach a point between Z and L we may have $AX > AZ$, and therefore greater than its supposed equal, BM; but BY cannot be greater than BM. Therefore we should have $AX > BY$, which is contrary to what is given.

Hence BM cannot be greater than AL, and similarly AL cannot be greater than BM. $\therefore AL = BM$.   Q. E. D.

208. Area of Circle. The area inclosed by a circle is called the *area of the circle.*

It is evident that a *diameter bisects the area of a circle.*

209. Segment. A portion of a plane bounded by an arc of a circle and its chord is called a *segment* of the circle.

If the chord is a diameter, the segment is called a *semicircle*, this word being commonly used to mean not only half of the circle but also the area inclosed by a semicircle and a diameter.

210. Sector. A portion of a plane bounded by two radii and the arc of the circle intercepted by the radii is called a *sector.*

If the arc is a quarter of the circle, the sector is called a *quadrant.*

211. Inscribed Angle. An angle whose vertex is on a circle, and whose sides are chords, is called an *inscribed angle.*

An angle is said to be *inscribed in a segment* if its vertex is on the arc of the segment and its sides pass through the ends of the arc.

Proposition XV. Theorem

212. *In the same circle or in equal circles two central angles have the same ratio as their intercepted arcs.*

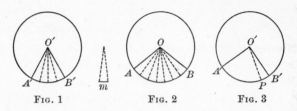

Fig. 1   Fig. 2   Fig. 3

Given two equal circles with centers O and O', AOB and $A'O'B'$ being central angles, and AB and $A'B'$ the intercepted arcs.

To prove that $\dfrac{\angle A'O'B'}{\angle AOB} = \dfrac{\text{arc } A'B'}{\text{arc } AB}.$

Case 1. *When the arcs are commensurable* (Figs. 1 and 2).

Proof. Let the arc m be a common measure of $A'B'$ and AB.

Apply the arc m as a measure to the arcs $A'B'$ and AB as many times as they will contain it.

Suppose m is contained a times in $A'B'$, and b times in AB.

Then $\dfrac{\text{arc } A'B'}{\text{arc } AB} = \dfrac{a}{b}.$

At the several points of division on AB and $A'B'$ draw radii.

These radii will divide $\angle AOB$ into b parts, and $\angle A'O'B'$ into a parts, equal each to each.   § 167

$$\therefore \frac{\angle A'O'B'}{\angle AOB} = \frac{a}{b}.$$

$$\therefore \frac{\angle A'O'B'}{\angle AOB} = \frac{\text{arc } A'B'}{\text{arc } AB}, \text{ by Ax. 8.}$$ Q.E.D.

Case 2 may be omitted at the discretion of the teacher if the incommensurable cases are not to be taken in the course.

CASE 2. *When the arcs are incommensurable* (Figs. 2 and 3).

Proof. Divide AB into a number of equal parts, and apply one of these parts to $A'B'$ as many times as $A'B'$ will contain it.

Since AB and $A'B'$ are incommensurable, a certain number of these parts will extend from A' to some point, as P, leaving a remainder PB' less than one of these parts. Draw $O'P$.

By construction AB and $A'P$ are commensurable.

$$\therefore \frac{\angle A'O'P}{\angle AOB} = \frac{\text{arc } A'P}{\text{arc } AB} \qquad \text{Case 1}$$

By increasing the *number* of equal parts into which AB is divided we can diminish the *length* of each, and therefore can make PB' less than any assigned positive value, however small.

Hence PB' approaches zero as a limit as the number of parts of AB is indefinitely increased, and at the same time the corresponding angle $PO'B'$ approaches zero as a limit. § 204

Therefore the arc $A'P$ approaches the arc $A'B'$ as a limit, and the $\angle A'O'P$ approaches the $\angle A'O'B'$ as a limit.

$$\therefore \text{ the variable } \frac{\text{arc } A'P}{\text{arc } AB} \text{ approaches } \frac{\text{arc } A'B'}{\text{arc } AB} \text{ as a limit,}$$

and the variable $\dfrac{\angle A'O'P}{\angle AOB}$ approaches $\dfrac{\angle A'O'B'}{\angle AOB}$ as a limit.

But $\dfrac{\angle A'O'P}{\angle AOB}$ is always equal to $\dfrac{\text{arc } A'P}{\text{arc } AB}$,

as $A'P$ varies in value and approaches $A'B'$ as a limit. Case 1

$$\therefore \frac{\angle A'O'B'}{\angle AOB} = \frac{\text{arc } A'B'}{\text{arc } AB}, \text{ by § 207.} \qquad \text{Q.E.D.}$$

213. Numerical Measure. We therefore see that the numerical measure of a central angle (in degrees, for example) equals the numerical measure of the intercepted arc. This is commonly expressed by saying that *a central angle is measured by the intercepted arc.*

PROPOSITION XVI. THEOREM

214. *An inscribed angle is measured by half the in·tercepted arc.*

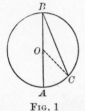 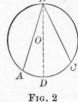 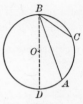

FIG. 1   FIG. 2   FIG. 3

Given a circle with center **O** and the inscribed angle **B**, intercepting the arc **AC**.

To prove that $\angle B$ *is measured by half the arc AC.*

CASE 1. *When O is on one side, as AB* (Fig. 1).

Proof.	Draw OC.	
Then	$\because OC = OB,$	§ 162
	$\therefore \angle B = \angle C.$	§ 74
But	$\angle B + \angle C = \angle AOC.$	§ 111
	$\therefore 2\angle B = \angle AOC.$	Ax. 9
	$\therefore \angle B = \frac{1}{2} \angle AOC.$	Ax. 4
But	$\angle AOC$ is measured by arc AC.	§ 213
	$\therefore \frac{1}{2} \angle AOC$ is measured by $\frac{1}{2}$ arc AC.	Ax. 4
	$\therefore \angle B$ is measured by $\frac{1}{2}$ arc AC.	Ax. 9

CASE 2. *When O lies within the angle B* (Fig. 2).

Proof.   Draw the diameter BD.

Then $\angle ABD$ is measured by $\frac{1}{2}$ arc AD,

and $\angle DBC$ is measured by $\frac{1}{2}$ arc DC.   Case 1

$\therefore \angle ABD + \angle DBC$ is measured by $\frac{1}{2}$ (arc AD + arc DC),

or $\angle ABC$ is measured by $\frac{1}{2}$ arc AC.

CASE 3. *When O lies outside the angle B* (Fig. 3).

Proof. Draw the diameter *BD*.

Then $\angle DBC$ is measured by $\frac{1}{2}$ arc *DC*,

and $\angle DBA$ is measured by $\frac{1}{2}$ arc *DA*. Case 1

∴ $\angle DBC - \angle DBA$ is measured by $\frac{1}{2}$ (arc *DC* − arc *DA*),

or $\angle ABC$ is measured by $\frac{1}{2}$ arc *AC*. Q.E.D.

FIG. 4

FIG. 5

FIG. 6

215. COROLLARY 1. *An angle inscribed in a semicircle is a right angle.*

For it is half of a central straight angle, as in Fig. 4.

216. COROLLARY 2. *An angle inscribed in a segment greater than a semicircle is an acute angle, and an angle inscribed in a segment less than a semicircle is an obtuse angle.*

See ∡ *A* and *B* in Fig. 5.

217. COROLLARY 3. *Angles inscribed in the same segment or in equal segments are equal.*

Why is this? (Fig. 6.)

218. COROLLARY 4. *If a quadrilateral is inscribed in a circle, the opposite angles are supplementary; and, conversely, if two opposite angles of a quadrilateral are supplementary, the quadrilateral can be inscribed in a circle.*

For the second part, can a circle be passed through *A*, *B*, *C* (§ 190)? If it does not pass through *D* also, can you show that $\angle D$ would be greater than or less than some other angle (§ 111) that is supplementary to $\angle B$?

EXERCISE 33

1. A parallelogram inscribed in a circle is a rectangle.

2. A trapezoid inscribed in a circle is isosceles.

3. The shorter segment of the diameter through a given point within a circle is the shortest line that can be drawn from that point to the circle.

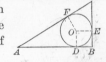

Let P be the given point. Prove PA shorter than any other line PX from P to the circle.

4. The longer segment of the diameter through a given point within a circle is the longest line that can be drawn from that point to the circle.

5. The diameter of the circle inscribed in a right triangle is equal to the difference between the hypotenuse and the sum of the other two sides.

6. A line from a given point outside a circle passing through the center contains the shortest line-segment that can be drawn from that point to the circle.

Let P be the point, O the center, A the point where PO cuts the circle, and C any other point on the circle. How does $PC + CO$ compare with PO?

7. A line from a given point outside a circle passing through the center contains the longest line-segment (to the concave arc) that can be drawn from that point to the circle.

8. Through one of the points of intersection of two circles a diameter of each circle is drawn. Prove that the line joining the ends of the diameters passes through the other point of intersection.

9. If two circles intersect and a line is drawn through each point of intersection terminated by the circles, the chords joining the corresponding ends of these lines are parallel.

Proposition XVII. Theorem

219. *An angle formed by two chords intersecting within the circle is measured by half the sum of the intercepted arcs.*

Given the angle *AOB* formed by the chords *AC* and *BD*.

To prove that ∠ *AOB is measured by* ½ (arc *AB* + arc *CD*).

Proof.   Draw *AD*.

Then   ∠ *AOB* = ∠ *A* + ∠ *D*.   § 111

(An exterior ∠ of a △ is equal to the sum of the two opposite interior ⦞.)

But ∠ *A* is measured by ½ arc *CD*,   § 214

(An inscribed ∠ is measured by half the intercepted arc.)

and ∠ *D* is measured by ½ arc *AB*.   § 214

∴ ∠ *AOB* is measured by ½ (arc *AB* + arc *CD*), by Ax. 1.   **q.e.d.**

Discussion. If *O* is at the center of the circle, to what previous proposition does this proposition reduce ?

If *O* is on the circle, as at *B*, to what previous proposition does this proposition reduce ?

Suppose the point *O* remains as in the figure, and the chord *AC* swings about *O* as a pivot until it coincides with the chord *BD*. What can then be said of the measure of ⦞ *AOB* and *COD* ? What can be said as to the measure of ⦞ *BOC* and *DOA* ?

It is also possible to prove the proposition by drawing a chord *AE* parallel to *BD*, and showing that ∠ *AOB* = ∠ *A*, since they are alternate-interior angles formed by a transversal cutting two parallels. Now ∠ *A* is measured by ½ arc *CE*. But arc *CE* = arc *CD* + arc *DE*, or arc *CD* + arc *AB*, since arc *AB* = arc *DE* (§ 189). Therefore ∠ *AOB*, which equals ∠ *A*, is measured by ½ (arc *AB* + arc *CD*).

Proposition XVIII. Theorem

220. *An angle formed by a tangent and a chord drawn from the point of contact is measured by half the intercepted arc.*

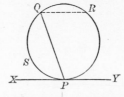

Given the chord *PQ* and the tangent *XY* through *P.*

To prove that ∠ QPX is measured by half the arc QSP.

Proof. Suppose the chord *QR* drawn from the point *Q* parallel to the tangent *XY.*

$$\text{Then arc } PR = \text{arc } QSP. \qquad \S\ 189$$

(*Two parallel lines intercept equal arcs on a circle.*)

$$\text{Also } \angle QPX = \angle PQR. \qquad \S\ 100$$

(*If two parallel lines are cut by a transversal, the alternate-interior angles are equal.*)

$$\text{But } \angle PQR \text{ is measured by } \tfrac{1}{2} \text{ arc } PR. \qquad \S\ 214$$

(*An inscribed ∠ is measured by half the intercepted arc.*)

Substitute ∠ *QPX* for its equal, the ∠ *PQR,*

and substitute arc *QSP* for its equal, the arc *PR.*

Then ∠ *QPX* is measured by $\tfrac{1}{2}$ arc *QSP,* by Ax. 9.   **Q. E D.**

Discussion. By half of what arc is ∠ *YPQ,* the supplement of ∠ *QPX,* measured ?

If *PQ* should be drawn so as to be perpendicular to *XY,* by what would ∠s *YPQ* and *QPX* be measured ?

Suppose *PQ* swings about the point *P* as a pivot until it coincides with *XY,* by what will ∠ *YPQ* be measured ? By what will ∠ *QPX* be measured, and what will it equal ?

Proposition XIX. Theorem

221. *An angle formed by two secants, a secant and a tangent, or two tangents, drawn to a circle from an external point, is measured by half the difference of the intercepted arcs.*

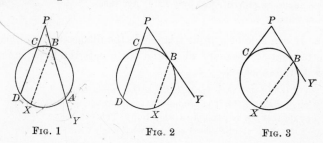

Fig. 1   Fig. 2   Fig. 3

Given two secants *PBA* and *PCD*, **from the external point** *P.*

To prove that ∠ *P is measured by* $\frac{1}{2}$ (*arc DA — arc BC*).

Proof. Suppose the chord *BX* drawn ‖ to *PCD* (Fig. 1).

Then   arc *BC* = arc *DX*.   § 189

Furthermore   arc *XA* = arc *DA* — arc *DX*.

         ∴ arc *XA* = arc *DA* — arc *BC*.   Ax. 9

Also   ∠ *P* = ∠ *XBA*.   § 102

         But ∠ *XBA* is measured by $\frac{1}{2}$ arc *XA*.   § 214

         Substitute ∠ *P* for its equal, the ∠ *XBA*,

and substitute arc *DA* — arc *BC* for its equal, the arc *XA*.

Then ∠ *P* is measured by $\frac{1}{2}$ (arc *DA* — arc *BC*), by Ax. 9. Q.E.D.

If the secant *PBAY* swings around to tangency, it becomes the tangent *PB* and Fig. 1 becomes Fig. 2. If the secant *PCD* also swings around to tangency, it becomes the tangent *PC* and Fig. 2 becomes Fig. 3. The proof of the theorem for each of these cases is left for the student.

EXERCISE 34

1. If two circles touch each other and two lines are drawn through the point of contact terminated by the circles, the chords joining the ends of these lines are parallel.

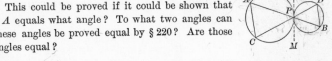

This could be proved if it could be shown that ∠ *A* equals what angle? To what two angles can these angles be proved equal by § 220? Are those angles equal?

2. If one side of a right triangle is the diameter of a circle, the tangent at the point where the circle cuts the hypotenuse bisects the other side.

If *OE* is ‖ to *AC*, then because *BO* = *OA*, what is the relation of *BE* to *EC*? The proposition therefore reduces to proving that *OE* is parallel to what line? This can be proved if ∠ *BOE* can be shown equal to what angle?

3. If from the extremities of a diameter *AD* two chords, *AC* and *DB*, are drawn intersecting at *P* so as to make ∠ *APB* = 45°, then ∠ *BOC* is a right angle.

4. The radius of the circle inscribed in an equilateral triangle is equal to one third the altitude of the triangle.

To prove this we must show that *AF* equals what line? It looks as if *AF* might equal *EF*, and *EF* equal *OF*. Is there any way of proving △ *OFE* equilateral? of proving △ *AEF* isosceles?

5. If two lines are drawn through any point in a diagonal of a square parallel to the sides, the points where these lines meet the sides lie on the circle whose center is the point of intersection of the diagonals.

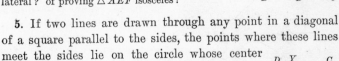

OY = *OZ* if what two ▵ are congruent? Why are these ▵ congruent? *OY* = *OX* if what two ▵ are congruent? *OX* = *OW* if what two ▵ are congruent?

222. Positive and Negative Quantities. In geometry, as in algebra, quantities may be distinguished as *positive* and as *negative*.

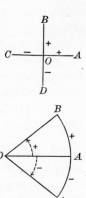

Thus as we consider temperature above zero positive and temperature below zero negative, so in this figure, if *OB* is considered *positive*, then *OD* may be considered *negative*. Similarly, if *OA* is considered positive, then *OC* may be considered negative.

Likewise with respect to angles and arcs, if the rotating line *OA* moves in the direction of *AB*, counterclockwise, the angle and arc generated are considered *positive*. If it rotates in the direction *AB'*, like the hands of a clock, the angle and arc generated are considered *negative*.

223. Principle of Continuity. By considering the distinction between positive and negative magnitudes, a theorem may often be so stated as to include several particular theorems. For example, *The angle included between two lines that cut or are tangent to a circle is measured by half the sum of the intercepted arcs.*

In particular: 1. If the lines intersect at the center, half the sum of the arcs will then become simply one of the arcs, and the proposition reduces to that of § 213.

2. If the lines are two general chords, we have the case of § 219.

3. If the point of intersection *P* moves to the circle, we have the case of § 214, one arc becoming zero.

4. If *P* moves outside the circle, then the smaller arc passes through zero and becomes negative, so that the sum of the arcs becomes their arithmetical difference (§ 221).

We may continue the discussion so as to include all the cases of the propositions proved from § 213 to § 221.

When the reasoning employed to prove a theorem is continued as just illustrated, so as to include several theorems, we are said to reason by the *Principle of Continuity*.

✓ **224. Problems of Construction.** At the beginning of the study of geometry some directions were given for simple constructions, so that figures might be drawn with accuracy. It was not proved at that time that these constructions were correct, because no theorems had been studied on which proofs could be based. It is now purposed to review these constructions, to prove that they are correct, and to apply the methods employed to the solution of more difficult problems.

225. Nature of a Solution. A solution of a problem has one requirement that a proof of a theorem does not have.

In a theorem we have three general steps: (1) *Given*, (2) *To prove*, (3) *Proof*. In a problem we have four steps: (1) *Given*, (2) *Required* (to do some definite thing), (3) *Construction* (showing how to do it), (4) *Proof* (that the construction is correct).

We *prove* a theorem, but we *solve* a problem, and then prove that our solution is a correct one.

In the figures of this text given lines are shown as full, black lines; construction lines and lines required are shown as dotted lines.

226. Discussion of a Problem. Besides the four necessary general steps in treating a problem, there is a desirable step to be taken in many cases. This is the discussion of the problem, in which is considered whether there is more than one solution, and other similar questions.

For example, suppose the problem is this: *Required from a given point to draw a tangent to a circle.*

After the problem has been solved we may discuss it thus: In general, if the given point is outside the circle, two tangents may be drawn, and these tangents are equal (§ 192); if the given point is on the circle only one tangent can be drawn, since only one perpendicular can be drawn to a radius at its extremity (§ 184); if the given point is within the circle, evidently no tangent can be drawn.

In the discussion the Principle of Continuity often enters, the figure being studied for various positions of some given point or line, as was done in the discussions on pages 121 and 122.

Proposition XX. Problem

227. *To let fall a perpendicular upon a given line from a given external point.*

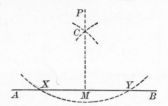

Given the line AB and the external point P.

Required from P to let fall a $\perp$ upon AB.

Construction. With P as a center, and a radius sufficiently great, describe an arc cutting AB at X and Y.   Post. 4

With X and Y as centers, and a convenient radius, describe two arcs intersecting at C.   Post. 4

Draw PC.   Post. 1

Produce PC to intersect AB at M.   Post. 2

Then PM is the line required.   Q. E. F.

Proof. Since P and C are by construction two points each equidistant from X and Y, they determine the perpendicular to XY at its mid-point.   § 151

(*Two points each equidistant from the extremities of a line determine the $\perp$ bisector of the line.*)   Q. E. D.

Discussion. The following are interesting considerations :

That PC produced will really intersect AB, as stated in the construction, is shown in the proof.

A convenient radius to take for the two intersecting arcs is XY.

If C falls on P, take C at the other intersection of the arcs below AB, as is seen in the figure of Ex. 2, p. 9.

To obtain a radius for the first circle, draw any line from P that will cut AB, and use that.

Proposition XXI. Problem

228. *At a given point in a given line, to erect a perpendicular to the line.*

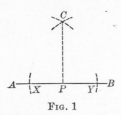

Fig. 1

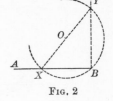

Fig. 2

Given the point *P* in the line *AB*.

Required to erect a ⊥ to AB at P.

Case 1. *When the point P is not at the end of AB* (Fig. 1).

Construction. Take $PX = PY$. Post. 4

With *X* and *Y* as centers, and a convenient radius, describe arcs intersecting at *C*. Post. 4

Draw *CP*. Post. 1

Then *CP* is ⊥ to *AB*. Q.E.F.

Proof. *P* and *C*, two points each equidistant from *X* and *Y*, determine the ⊥ bisector of *XY*, by § 151. Q.E.D.

Case 2. *When the point P is at the end of AB* (Fig. 2).

Construction. Suppose *P* to coincide with *B*.

Take any point *O* outside of *AB*, and with *O* as a center and *OB* as a radius describe a circle intersecting *AB* at *X*.

From *X* draw the diameter *XY*, and draw *BY*. Post. 1

Then *BY* is ⊥ to *AB*. Q.E.F.

Proof. ∠*B* is a right angle. § 215

∴ *BY* is ⊥ to *AB*, by § 27. Q.E.D.

Discussion. If the circle described with *O* as a center is tangent to *AB* at *B*, then *OB* is the required perpendicular (§ 185).

Proposition XXII.   Problem

229. *To bisect a given line.*

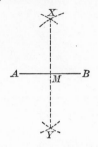

Given the line *AB*.

Required to bisect AB.

Construction. With *A* and *B* as centers and *AB* as a radius describe arcs intersecting at *X* and *Y*, and draw *XY*.   Post. 4

Then *XY* bisects *AB*.   Q. E. F.

Proof.   *XY* bisects *AB*, by § 151.   Q. E. D.

Proposition XXIII.   Problem

230. *To bisect a given arc.*

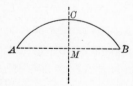

Given the arc *AB*.

Required to bisect AB.

Construction. Draw the chord *AB*.   Post. 1

Draw *CM*, the perpendicular bisector of the chord *AB*.   § 229

Then *CM* bisects the arc *AB*.   Q. E. F.

Proof.   *CM* bisects the arc *AB*, by § 177.   Q. E. D.

PROPOSITION XXIV. PROBLEM

231. *To bisect a given angle.*

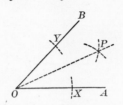

Given the angle *AOB*.

Required to bisect ∠ AOB.

Construction. With *O* as a center and any radius describe an arc cutting *OA* at *X* and *OB* at *Y*.   Post. 4

With *X* and *Y* as centers and *XY* as a radius describe arcs intersecting at *P*.   Post. 4

Draw *OP*.   Post. 1

Then *OP* bisects ∠ AOB.   Q.E.F.

Proof.   Draw *PX* and *PY*.

Then prove that the △ *OXP* and *OYP* are congruent.   § 80

Then ∠ AOP = ∠ POB, by § 67.   Q.E.D.

EXERCISE 35

1. To construct an angle of 45°; of 135°.

2. To construct an angle of 22° 30′; of 157° 30′.

3. To construct an equilateral triangle, having given one side, and thus to construct an angle of 60°.

4. To construct an angle of 30°; and thus to trisect a right angle.

5. To construct an angle of 15°; of 7° 30′; of 195°; of 345°.

6. To construct a triangle having two of its angles equal to 75°. Is the triangle definitely determined?

Proposition XXV. Problem

232. *From a given point in a given line, to draw a line making an angle equal to a given angle.*

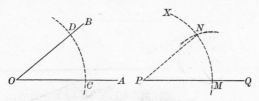

Given the angle *AOB* and the point *P* in the line *PQ*.

Required from P to draw a line making with the line PQ an angle equal to ∠AOB.

Construction. With *O* as a center and any radius describe an arc cutting *OA* at *C* and *OB* at *D*.   Post. 4

With *P* as a center and the same radius describe an arc *MX*, cutting *PQ* at *M*.   Post. 4

With *M* as a center and a line joining *C* and *D* as a radius describe an arc cutting the arc *MX* at *N*.   Post. 4

Draw *PN*.   Post. 1

Then ∠*QPN* = ∠*AOB*.   Q. E. F.

Proof.   Draw *CD* and *MN*.

Then prove that the △ *PMN* and *OCD* are congruent.   § 80

Then ∠*QPN* = ∠*AOB*, by § 67.   Q. E. D.

233. Corollary. *Through a given external point, to draw a line parallel to a given line.*

Let *AB* be the given line and *P* the given external point.

Draw any line *XPY* through *P*, cutting *AB* as in the figure.

Draw *CD* through *P*, making ∠*p* = ∠*q*.

The line *CD* will be the line required.

Proposition XXVI. Problem

234. *To divide a given line into a given number of equal parts.*

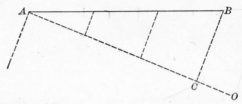

Given the line *AB*.

Required to divide AB into a given number of equal parts.

Construction. From *A* draw the line *AO*, making any convenient angle with *AB*.   Post. 1

Take any convenient length, and by describing arcs apply it to *AO* as many times as is indicated by the number of parts into which *AB* is to be divided.   Post. 4

From *C*, the last point thus found on *AO*, draw *CB*.   Post. 1

From the division points on *AO* draw parallels to *CB*.   § 233

These lines divide *AB* into equal parts.   Q. E. F.

Proof. These lines divide *AB* into equal parts, by § 134.   Q. E. D.

EXERCISE 36

1. To divide a given line into four equal parts.

2. To construct an equilateral triangle, given the perimeter.

3. Through a given point, to draw a line which shall make equal angles with the two sides of a given angle.

4. Through a given point, to draw two lines so that they shall form with two intersecting lines two isosceles triangles.

5. To construct a triangle having its three angles respectively equal to the three angles of a given triangle.

Proposition XXVII. Problem

235. *To construct a triangle when two sides and the included angle are given.*

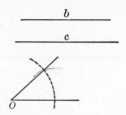 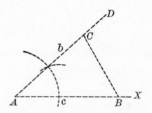

Given *b* and *c* two sides of a triangle, and *O* the included angle.

Required to construct the triangle.

Construction. On any line as *AX*, by describing an arc, mark off *AB* equal to *c*.   Post. 4

At *A* construct ∠ *BAD* equal to ∠ *O*.   § 232

On *AD*, by describing an arc, mark off *AC* equal to *b*.   Post. 4

Draw *BC*.   Post. 1

Then △ *ABC* is the △ required.   Q. E. F.

Proof. (Left for the student.)

236. Corollary 1. *To construct a triangle when a side and two angles are given.*

There are two cases to be considered: (1) when the given side is included between the given angles; and (2) when it is not (in which case find the other angle by § 107).

237. Corollary 2. *To construct a triangle when the three sides are given.*

238. Corollary 3. *To construct a parallelogram when two sides and the included angle are given.*

Combine § 235 and § 233.

Proposition XXVIII. Problem

239. *To construct a triangle when two sides and the angle opposite one of them are given.*

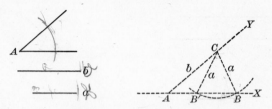

Given a and b two sides of a triangle, and A the angle opposite a.

Required to construct the triangle.

Construction. Case 1. *If a is less than b.*

Construct $\angle XAY$ equal to the given $\angle A$.   § 232

On AY take AC equal to b.

From C as a center, with a radius equal to a, describe an arc intersecting the line AX at B and B'.

Draw BC and $B'C$, thus completing the triangle.

Then both the $\triangle ABC$ and $AB'C$ satisfy the conditions, and hence we have two constructions.   Q.E.F.

This is called the *ambiguous* case.

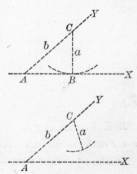

Discussion. If the given side a is equal to the $\perp CB$, the arc described from C will touch AX, and there will be but one construction, the rt. $\triangle ABC$.

If the given side a is less than the perpendicular from C, the arc described from C will not intersect or touch AX, and hence a construction is impossible.

If $\angle A$ is right or obtuse, a construction is impossible, since $a < b$; for the side of a triangle opposite a right or obtuse angle is the longest side (§ 114).

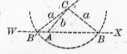

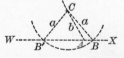

Case 2. *If a is equal to b.*

If the given $\angle A$ is acute, and $a = b$, the arc described from C as a center, and with a radius equal to a, will cut the line WX at the points A and B. There is therefore but one triangle that satisfies the conditions, namely the isosceles $\triangle ABC$.

Discussion. If the $\angle A$ is right or obtuse, a construction is impossible when $a = b$; for equal sides of a triangle have equal angles opposite them, and a triangle cannot have two right angles or two obtuse angles (§ 109).

Case 3. *If a is greater than b.*

If the given $\angle A$ is acute, the arc described from C will cut the line WX on opposite sides of A, at B and B'. The $\triangle ABC$ satisfies the conditions, but the $\triangle AB'C$ does not, for it does not contain the acute $\angle A$. There is then only one triangle that satisfies the conditions, namely the $\triangle ABC$.

If the given $\angle A$ is right, the arc described from C cuts the line WX on opposite sides of A at the points B and B', and we have the two *congruent* right triangles ABC and $AB'C$ that satisfy the conditions.

If the given $\angle A$ is obtuse, the arc described from C cuts the line WX on opposite sides of A, at the points B and B'. The $\triangle ABC$ satisfies the conditions, but the $\triangle AB'C$ does not, for it does not contain the obtuse $\angle A$. There is then only one triangle that satisfies the conditions, namely the $\triangle ABC$.

Discussion. We therefore see that when $a > b$, we have only one triangle that satisfies the conditions, for the two congruent right triangles give us only one distinct triangle.

Proposition XXIX. Problem

240. *To circumscribe a circle about a given triangle.*

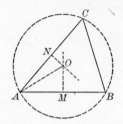

Given the triangle *ABC*.

Required to circumscribe a ⊙ about △ ABC.

Construction. Draw the perpendicular bisectors of the sides
AB and *AC*.   § 229

Since *AB* is not the prolongation of *CA*, these ⟂s will intersect at some point *O*. Otherwise they would be ∥, and one of
them would have to be ⟂ to two intersecting lines.   § 82

With *O* as a center, and a radius *OA*, describe a circle. Post. 4

The ⊙ *ABC* is the ⊙ required.   Q.E.F.

Proof. The point *O* is equidistant from *A* and *B*, and also is
equidistant from *A* and *C*.   § 150

∴ the point *O* is equidistant from *A*, *B*, and *C*.

∴ a ⊙ described with *O* as a center, with a radius equal to *OA*,
will pass through the vertices *A*, *B*, and *C*, by § 160.   Q.E.D.

241. Corollary 1. *To describe a circle through three points
not in the same straight line.*

242. Corollary 2. *To find the center of a given circle or
of the circle of which an arc is given.*

243. Circumcenter. The center of the circle circumscribed
about a polygon is called the *circumcenter* of the polygon.

PROPOSITION XXX. PROBLEM

244. *To inscribe a circle in a given triangle.*

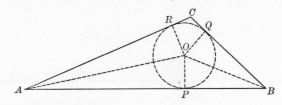

Given the triangle *ABC*.

Required to inscribe a ⊙ in △ABC.

Construction.   Bisect the ∠s *A* and *B*.   § 231

From *O*, the intersection of the bisectors, draw *OP* ⊥ to the side *AB*.   § 227

With *O* as a center and a radius *OP*, describe the ⊙ *PQR*.

The ⊙ *PQR* is the ⊙ required.   Q.E.F.

Proof. Since *O* is in the bisector of the ∠ *A*, it is equidistant from the sides *AB* and *AC*; and since *O* is in the bisector of the ∠ *B*, it is equidistant from the sides *AB* and *BC*.   § 152

∴ a circle described with *O* as a center, and a radius *OP*, will touch the sides of the triangle, by § 184.   Q.E.D.

245. Incenters and Excenters. The center of a circle inscribed in a polygon is called the *incenter* of the polygon.

The intersections of the bisectors of the exterior angles of a triangle are the centers of three circles, each tangent to one side of the triangle and the two other sides produced. These three circles are called *escribed* circles; and their centers are called the *excenters* of the triangle.

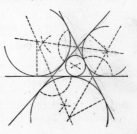

Proposition XXXI. Problem

246. *Through a given point, to draw a tangent to a given circle.*

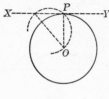

Fig. 1

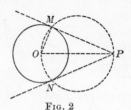

Fig. 2

Given the point *P* and the circle with center *O*.

Required through P to draw a tangent to the circle.

Case 1. *When the given point is on the circle* (Fig. 1).

Construction. From the center *O* draw the radius *OP*.   Post. 1

Through *P* draw *XY* ⊥ to *OP*.   § 228

Then *XY* is the tangent required.   Q.E.F.

Proof.   Since *XY* is ⊥ to the radius *OP*,   Const.

∴ *XY* is tangent to the ⊙ at *P*, by § 184.   Q.E.D.

Case 2. *When the given point is outside the circle* (Fig. 2).

Construction.   Draw *OP*.   Post. 1

Bisect *OP*.   § 229

With the mid-point of *OP* as a center and a radius equal to ½ *OP*, describe a circle intersecting the given circle at the points *M* and *N*, and draw *PM*.

Then *PM* is the tangent required.   Q.E.F.

Proof.   Draw *OM*.

∠ *OMP* is a right angle.   § 215

∴ *PM* is ⊥ to *OM*.   § 27

∴ *PM* is tangent to the circle at *M*, by § 184.   Q.E.D.

Discussion. In like manner, we may prove *PN* tangent to the given ⊙.

PROPOSITION XXXII. PROBLEM

247. *Upon a given line as a chord, to describe a segment of a circle in which a given angle may be inscribed.*

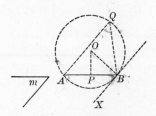

Given the line *AB* and the angle *m*.

Required on AB as a chord, to describe a segment of a circle in which ∠ m may be inscribed.

Construction. Construct the ∠ *ABX* equal to the ∠ *m*. § 232

Bisect the line *AB* by the ⊥ *PO*. § 229

From the point *B* draw *BO* ⊥ to *XB*. § 228

With *O*, the point of intersection of *PO* and *BO*, as a center, and a radius equal to *OB*, describe a circle.

The segment *ABQ* is the segment required. Q. E. F.

Proof. The point *O* is equidistant from *A* and *B*. § 150

∴ the circle will pass through *A* and *B*. § 160

But *BX* is ⊥ to *OB*. Const.

∴ *BX* is tangent to the ⊙. § 184

∴ ∠ *ABX* is measured by ½ arc *AB*. § 220

But any angle, as the ∠ *Q*, inscribed in the segment *ABQ* is measured by ½ arc *AB*. § 214

∴ ∠ *Q* = ∠ *ABX*. Ax. 8

But ∠ *ABX* = ∠ *m*. Const.

∴ ∠ *m* may be inscribed in the segment *ABQ*, by § 217. Q. E. D.

248. How to attack a Problem. There are three common methods by which to attack a new problem:

> (1) By synthesis;
> (2) By analysis;
> (3) By the intersection of loci.

249. Synthetic Method. If a problem is so simple that the solution is obvious from a known proposition, we have only to make the construction according to the proposition, and then to give the synthetic proof, if a proof is necessary, that the construction is correct.

It is rarely the case, however, that a problem is so simple as to allow this method to be used. We therefore commonly resort at once to the second method.

250. Analytic Method. This is the usual method of attack, and is as follows:

(1) Suppose the problem solved and see what results follow.

(2) Then see if it is possible to attain these results and thus effect the required construction; in other words, try to work backwards.

The third method, by the intersection of loci, is considered on page 143.

251. Determinate, Indeterminate, and Impossible Cases. A problem that has a definite number of solutions is said to be *determinate*. A problem that has an indefinite number of solutions is said to be *indeterminate*. A problem that has no solution is said to be *impossible*.

For example, to construct a triangle, having given its sides, is determinate; to construct a quadrilateral, having given its sides, is indeterminate; to construct a triangle with sides 2 in., 3 in., and 6 in. is impossible.

252. Discussion. The examination of a problem with reference to all possible conditions, particularly with respect to the number of solutions, is called the *discussion* of the problem.

Discussions have been given in several of the preceding problems.

253. Applications of the Analytic Method. The following are examples of the use of analysis in the solution of problems.

1. In a triangle ABC, to draw PQ parallel to the base AB, cutting the sides in P and Q, so that PQ shall equal $AP + BQ$.

Analysis. Assume the problem solved.

Then AP must equal some part of PQ, as PX, and BQ must equal QX.

But if $AP = PX$, what must $\angle PXA$ equal?

$\therefore PQ$ is ∥ to AB, what does $\angle PXA$ equal?

Then why must $\angle BAX = \angle XAP$?

Similarly, what about $\angle QBX$ and $\angle XBA$?

Construction. Now reverse the process. What should we do to ∠s A and B in order to fix X? Then how shall PQ be drawn? Now give the proof.

2. To construct a triangle, having given the perimeter, one angle, and the altitude from the vertex of the given angle.

Analysis. Let ABC be the triangle, $\angle C$ the given angle, and CP the given altitude, and assume that the problem is solved.

Since the perimeter is given as a definite line, we now try producing AB and BA, making $BN = BC$, and $AM = AC$.

Then $\angle m =$ what angle, and $\angle n =$ what angle?

Then $\angle m + \angle n + \angle MCN = 180°$.

But $\angle MCN = \angle m' + \angle ACB + \angle n'$.

$\therefore 2\angle m + 2\angle n + \angle ACB = 180°$. (Why?)

$\therefore \angle m + \angle n + \tfrac{1}{2}\angle ACB = 90°$,

or $\angle m + \angle n = 90° - \tfrac{1}{2}\angle ACB$.

$\therefore \angle MCN = 90° + \tfrac{1}{2}\angle ACB$. (Why?)

$\therefore \angle MCN$ is known.

Construction. Now reverse the process. Draw MN equal to the perimeter. Then on MN construct a segment in which $\angle MCN$ may be inscribed (§ 247). Draw XC ∥ to MN at the distance CP from MN, cutting the arc at C. Then A and B are on the ⊥ bisectors of CM and CN. **Why?**

3. To draw through two sides of a triangle a line parallel
to the third side, so that the part intercepted
between the sides shall have a given length.

If $PQ = d$, what does AR equal? How will you
reverse the reasoning?

4. To draw a tangent to a given circle so that it shall be
parallel to a given line.

5. To construct a triangle, having given a side, an adjacent
angle, and the difference of the other sides.

If AB, $\angle A$, and $AC - BC$ are known, what points are
determined? Then can XB be drawn? What kind of a triangle is $\triangle XBC$? How can C be located?

6. To construct a triangle, having given two angles and
the sum of two sides.

Can the third $\angle$ be found? Assume the problem solved. If $AX = AB + BC$, what kind of a
triangle is $\triangle BXC$? What does $\angle CBA$ equal?
Is $\angle X$ known? How can C be fixed?

7. To construct a square, having given the diagonal.

8. To draw through a given point P between the sides of
an angle AOB a line terminated by the sides
of the angle and bisected at P.

If $PM = PN$, and PR is $\parallel$ to AO, what can you
say as to OR and RN? Can you now reverse this?
Similarly, if PQ is $\parallel$ to BO, is $OQ =$ to QM?

9. To draw a line that would bisect the angle formed by
two lines if those lines were produced to meet.

If AB and CD are the given lines, consider what would be the conditions if they could be produced to meet at O. Then the
bisector of $\angle O$ would be the $\perp$ bisector of PQ, a line drawn
so as to make equal angles with the two given lines.

Now reverse this. How can we draw PQ so as to make
$\angle P = \angle Q$? Draw $BR \parallel$ to DC, and lay off $BR = BQ$.
Then draw QRP and prove that this is such a line. Then
draw its $\perp$ bisector.

254. Intersection of Loci. The third general method of attack mentioned in § 248 is by intersection of loci. This is very convenient when we wish to find a point satisfying two conditions, each of which involves some locus.

Wed.

EXERCISE 38

1. To find a point that is $\frac{1}{4}$ in. from a given point and $\frac{3}{16}$ in. from a given line.

If P is the given point, what is the locus of a point $\frac{1}{4}$ in. from P? If AB is the given line, what is the locus of a point $\frac{3}{16}$ in. from AB? These two loci intersect in how many points at most? Discuss the solution.

2. To find a point that is $\frac{1}{2}$ in. from one given point and $\frac{3}{4}$ in. from another given point.

Discuss the number of possible points answering the conditions.

3. To find a point that is $\frac{1}{2}$ in. from the vertex of an angle and equidistant from the sides of the angle.

4. To find a point that is equidistant from two intersecting lines and $\frac{1}{4}$ in. from their point of intersection.

How many such points can always be found?

5. To find a point that is $\frac{1}{2}$ in. from a given point and equidistant from two intersecting lines.

Discuss the problem for various positions of the given point.

6. To find a point that is $\frac{1}{2}$ in. from a given point and equidistant from two parallel lines.

Discuss the problem for various positions of the given point.

7. Find the locus of the mid-point of a chord of a given length that can be drawn in a given circle.

8. Find the locus of the mid-point of a chord drawn through a given point within a given circle.

9. To describe a circle that shall pass through a given point and cut equal chords of a given length from two parallels.

Analysis. Let A be the given point, BC and DE the given parallels, MN the given length, and O the center of the required circle.

Since the circle cuts equal chords from two parallels, what must be the relative distance of its center from each? Therefore what line must be one locus for O?

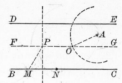

Draw the $\perp$ bisector of MN, cutting FG at P. How, then, does PM compare with the radius of the circle required? How shall we then find a point O on FG that is at a distance PM from A? Do we then know that O is the center of the required circle?

10. To describe a circle that shall be tangent to each of two given intersecting lines.

11. To find in a given line a point that is equidistant from two given points.

12. To find a point that is equidistant from two given points and at a given distance from a third given point.

13. To describe a circle that has a given radius and passes through two given points.

14. To find a point at given distances from two given points.

15. To describe a circle that has its center in a given line and passes through two given points.

16. To find a point that is equidistant from two given points and also equidistant from two given intersecting lines.

17. To find a point that is equidistant from two given points and also equidistant from two given parallel lines.

18. To find a point that is equidistant from two given intersecting lines and at a given distance from a given point.

19. To find a point that lies in one side of a given triangle and is equidistant from the other two sides.

255. General Directions for solving Problems. In attacking a new problem draw the most general figure possible and the solution may be evident at once. If the solution is not evident, see if it depends on finding a point, in which case see if two loci can be found. If this is not the case, assume the problem solved and try to work backwards,—the method of analysis.

EXERCISE 39

1. To draw a common tangent to two given circles.

If the centers are O and O' and the radii r and r', the tangent QR seems to be ‖ to $O'M$, a tangent from O' to a circle whose radius is $r - r'$. If this is true, we can easily reverse the process. Since there are two tangents from O', so there are two common tangents.

In the right-hand figure the tangent QR seems to be ‖ to $O'M$, a tangent from O' to a circle whose radius is $r + r'$. If this is true, we can easily reverse the process. There are four common tangents in general.

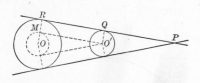
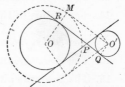

2. To draw a common tangent to two given circles, using the following figures.

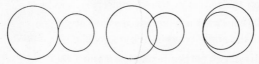

3. The locus of the vertex of a right triangle, having a given hypotenuse as its base, is the circle described upon the given hypotenuse as a diameter.

4. The locus of the vertex of a triangle, having a given base and a given angle at the vertex, is the arc which forms with the base a segment in which the given angle may be inscribed.

To construct an isosceles triangle, having given:

5. The base and the angle at the vertex.

6. The base and the radius of the circumscribed circle.

7. The base and the radius of the inscribed circle.

8. The perimeter and the altitude.

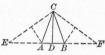

Let *ABC* be the △ required, *EF* the given perimeter. The altitude *CD* passes through the middle of *EF*, and the ▲ *EAC*, *BFC* are isosceles.

To construct a right triangle, having given:

9. The hypotenuse and one side.

10. One side and the altitude upon the hypotenuse.

11. The median and the altitude upon the hypotenuse.

12. The hypotenuse and the altitude upon the hypotenuse.

13. The radius of the inscribed circle and one side.

14. The radius of the inscribed circle and an acute angle.

To construct a triangle, having given:

15. The base, the altitude, and an angle at the base.

16. The base, the altitude, and the angle at the vertex.

17. One side, an adjacent angle, and the sum of the other sides.

18. To construct an equilateral triangle, having given the radius of the circumscribed circle.

19. To construct a rectangle, having given one side and the angle between the diagonals.

20. Given two perpendiculars, *AB* and *CD*, intersecting in *O*, and a line intersecting these perpendiculars in *E* and *F*; to construct a square, one of whose angles shall coincide with one of the right angles at *O*, and the vertex of the opposite angle of the square shall lie in *EF*. (Two solutions.)

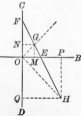

21. A straight rod moves so that its ends constantly touch two fixed rods perpendicular to each other. Find the locus of its mid-point.

22. A line moves so that it remains parallel to a given line, and so that one end lies on a given circle. Find the locus of the other end.

23. Find the locus of the midpoint of a line-segment that is drawn from a given external point to a given circle.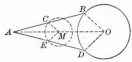

24. To draw lines from two given points P and Q which shall meet on a given line AB and make equal angles with AB.

$\because \angle BEQ = \angle PEC$, $\therefore \angle CEP' = \angle PEC$. (Why ?)

But it is easy to make $\angle CEP' = \angle PEC$, by making $PP' \perp AB$, and $CP' = PC$, and joining P' and Q.

25. To find the shortest path from a point P to a line AB and thence to a point Q.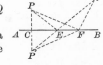

Prove that $PE + EQ < PF + FQ$, where $\angle BEQ = \angle PEC$.

This shows that a ray of light from a point to a plane mirror and thence to another point takes the shortest possible path.

26. The bisectors of the angles included by the opposite sides (produced) of an inscribed quadrilateral intersect at right angles.

Arc AX − arc MD
     = arc XB − arc CM. (Why ?)

Arc YA − arc BN
     = arc DY − arc NC. (Why ?)

$\therefore$ arc YX + arc NM
     = arc MY + arc XN. (Why ?)

$\therefore \angle YIX = \angle XIN$. (Why ?)

How does this prove the proposition ? Discuss the impossible case.

27. Construct this design, making the figure twice this size.

Construct the equilateral △. Then describe the small ⊚ with half the side of the △ as a radius. Then find the radius of the circumscribing ⊙.

28. A circular window in a church has a design similar to the accompanying figure. Draw it, making the figure twice this size.

This is made from the figure of the preceding exercise, by erasing certain lines.

29. Two wheels of radii 1 ft. 6 in. and 2 ft. 3 in. respectively are connected by a belt, drawn straight between the points of tangency. The centers being 6 ft. apart, draw the figure mathematically. Use the scale of 1 in. to the foot.

30. A water wheel is broken and all but a fragment is lost. A workman wishes to restore the wheel. Make a drawing showing how he can construct a wheel the size of the original.

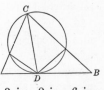

31. In this figure ∠m = 62°, and ∠n = 28°. Find the number of degrees in each of the other angles, and determine whether AB is a diameter.

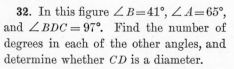

32. In this figure ∠B = 41°, ∠A = 65°, and ∠BDC = 97°. Find the number of degrees in each of the other angles, and determine whether CD is a diameter.

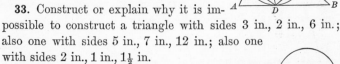

33. Construct or explain why it is impossible to construct a triangle with sides 3 in., 2 in., 6 in.; also one with sides 5 in., 7 in., 12 in.; also one with sides 2 in., 1 in., 1½ in.

34. Show how to draw a tangent to this circle P at the point P, the center of the circle not being accessible.

EXERCISE 40

1. In a circle whose center is O the chord AB is drawn so that $\angle BAO = 27°$. How many degrees are there in $\angle AOB$?

2. In a circle whose center is O the chord AB is drawn so that $\angle BAO = 25°$. On the circle, and on the same side of AB as the center O, the point D is taken and is joined to A and B. How many degrees are there in $\angle ADB$?

3. What is the locus of the mid-point of a chord of a circle formed by secants drawn from a given external point?

4. In a circle whose center is O two perpendiculars OM and ON are drawn to the chords AB and CD respectively, and it is known that $\angle NMO = \angle ONM$. Prove that $AB = CD$.

5. Two circles intersect at the points A and B. Through A a variable secant is drawn, cutting the circles at C and D. Prove that the angle DBC is constant.

6. Let A and B be two fixed points on a given circle, and M and N be the extremities of a rotating diameter of the same circle. Find the locus of the point of intersection of the lines AM and BN.

7. Upon a line AB a segment of a circle containing 240° is constructed, and in the segment any chord PQ subtending an arc of 60° is drawn. Find the locus of the point of intersection of AP and BQ; also of AQ and BP.

8. To construct a square, given the sum of the diagonal and one side.

Let $ABCD$ be the square required, and CA the di- agonal. Produce CA, making $AE = AB$. $\triangle ABC$ and ABE are isosceles and $\angle BAC = \angle ACB = 45°$. Find the value of $\angle E$. Construct $\angle CBE$. Now reverse the reasoning.

The propositions in Exercise 40 are taken from recent college entrance examination papers.

Friday

EXERCISE 41

Review Questions

1. Define the word *circle* and the principal terms used in connection with it.

2. What is meant by a central angle ? How is it measured ?

3. What is meant by an inscribed angle? How is it measured?

4. State the general proposition covering all the cases that have been considered relating to the measure of an angle formed by the intersection of two secants.

5. State all of the facts you have learned relating to equal chords of a circle.

6. State all of the facts you have learned relating to unequal chords of a circle.

7. State all of the facts you have learned relating to tangents to a circle.

8. How many points are required to determine a straight line ? two parallel lines ? an angle ? a circle ?

9. Name one kind of magnitude that you have learned to trisect, and state how you proceed to trisect this magnitude.

10. In order to construct a definite triangle, what parts must be known ?

11. What are the important methods of attacking a new problem in geometry ? Which is the best method to try first ?

12. What is meant by determinate, indeterminate, and impossible cases in the solution of a problem ?

13. Distinguish between a constant and a variable, and give an illustration of each.

14. Distinguish between inscribed, circumscribed, and escribed circles.

15. What is meant by the statement that a central angle is measured by the intercepted arc ?

True.

BOOK III

PROPORTION. SIMILAR POLYGONS

256. Proportion. An expression of equality between two equal ratios is called a *proportion*.

257. Symbols. A proportion is written in one of the following forms: $\dfrac{a}{b} = \dfrac{c}{d}$; $a : b = c : d$; $a : b :: c : d$.

This proportion is read "*a* is to *b* as *c* is to *d*"; or "the ratio of *a* to *b* is equal to the ratio of *c* to *d*."

258. Terms. In a proportion the four quantities compared are called the *terms*. The first and third terms are called the *antecedents;* the second and fourth terms, the *consequents*. The first and fourth terms are called the *extremes;* the second and third terms, the *means*.

Thus in the proportion $a : b = c : d$, *a* and *c* are the antecedents, *b* and *d* the consequents, *a* and *d* the extremes, *b* and *c* the means.

259. Fourth Proportional. The fourth term of a proportion is called the *fourth proportional* to the terms taken in order.

Thus in the proportion $a : b = c : d$, *d* is the fourth proportional to *a*, *b*, and *c*.

260. Continued Proportion. The quantities *a, b, c, d,* $\cdots$ are said to be in *continued proportion*, if $a : b = b : c = c : d = \cdots$.

If three quantities are in continued proportion, the second is called the *mean proportional* between the other two, and the third is called the *third proportional* to the other two.

Thus in the proportion $a : b = b : c$, *b* is the mean proportional between *a* and *c*, and *c* is the third proportional to *a* and *b*.

Proposition I. Theorem

261. *In any proportion the product of the extremes is equal to the product of the means.*

Given $\qquad\qquad\qquad a : b = c : a.$

To prove that $\qquad\qquad ad = bc.$

Proof. $\qquad\qquad\qquad \dfrac{a}{b} = \dfrac{c}{d}.$ $\qquad\qquad$ § 257

Multiplying by bd, $\qquad ad = bc$, by Ax. 3. $\qquad$ Q.E.D.

262. Corollary 1. *The mean proportional between two quantities is equal to the square root of their product.*

For if $a : b = b : c$, then $b^2 = ac$ (§ 261), and $b = \sqrt{ac}$, by Ax. 5.

263. Corollary 2. *If the two antecedents of a proportion are equal, the two consequents are equal.*

264. Corollary 3. *If the product of two quantities is equal to the product of two others, either two may be made the extremes of a proportion in which the other two are made the means.*

For if $ad = bc$, then, by dividing by bd, $\dfrac{a}{b} = \dfrac{c}{d}$, by Ax. 4.

Proposition II. Theorem

265. *If four quantities are in proportion, they are in proportion by alternation ; that is, the first term is to the third as the second term is to the fourth.*

Given $\qquad\qquad\qquad a : b = c : d.$

To prove that $\qquad\qquad a : c = b : d.$

Proof. $\qquad\qquad\qquad ad = bc.$ $\qquad\qquad$ § 261

Dividing by cd, $\qquad\qquad \dfrac{a}{c} = \dfrac{b}{d},$ $\qquad\qquad$ Ax. 4

or $\qquad\qquad\qquad a : c = b : d$, by § 257. $\qquad$ Q.E.D.

PROPOSITION III. THEOREM

266. *If four quantities are in proportion, they a[r]e in proportion by inversion ; that is, the second term is [to] the first as the fourth term is to the third.*

Given $\qquad\qquad a : b = c : d.$

To prove that $\qquad b : a = d : c.$

Proof. $\qquad\qquad bc = ad.$ $\qquad\qquad$ § 261

Dividing each member of the equation by ac,

$$\frac{b}{a} = \frac{d}{c}, \qquad\qquad \text{Ax. 4}$$

or $\qquad b : a = d : c$, by § 257. $\qquad\qquad$ Q. E. D.

PROPOSITION IV. THEOREM

267. *If four quantities are in proportion, they are in proportion by composition; that is, the sum of the first two terms is to the second term as the sum of the last two terms is to the fourth term.*

Given $\qquad\qquad a : b = c : d.$

To prove that $\qquad a + b : b = c + d : d.$

Proof. $\qquad\qquad \frac{a}{b} = \frac{c}{d}.$ $\qquad\qquad$ § 257

Adding 1 to each member of the equation,

$$\frac{a}{b} + 1 = \frac{c}{d} + 1, \qquad\qquad \text{Ax. 1}$$

or $\qquad \frac{a+b}{b} = \frac{c+d}{d}.$

$\therefore a + b : b = c + d : d$, by § 257. $\qquad$ Q. E. D.

In a similar manner it may be shown that
$$a + b : a = c + d : c.$$

PROPOSITION V. THEOREM

es are in proportion, they are in
; that is, the difference of the
he second term as the difference
is to the fourth term.

$a : b = c : d.$

$b : b = c - d : d.$

Proof. $\dfrac{a}{b} = \dfrac{c}{d}.$ § 257

$$\therefore \frac{a}{b} - 1 = \frac{c}{d} - 1, \qquad \text{Ax. 2}$$

or $\dfrac{a - b}{b} = \dfrac{c - d}{d}.$

$\therefore a - b : b = c - d : d$, by § 257.   Q. E. D.

In a similar manner it may be shown that

$$a - b : a = c - d : c.$$

PROPOSITION VI. THEOREM

269. *In a series of equal ratios, the sum of the antecedents is to the sum of the consequents as any antecedent is to its consequent.*

Given $a : b = c : d = e : f = g : h.$

To prove that $a + c + e + g : b + d + f + h = a : b.$

Proof. Let $r = \dfrac{a}{b} = \dfrac{c}{d} = \dfrac{e}{f} = \dfrac{g}{h}.$

Then $a = br, \quad c = dr, \quad e = fr, \quad g = hr.$ Ax. 3

$\therefore a + c + e + g = (b + d + f + h)r.$ Ax. 1

$\therefore \dfrac{a + c + e + g}{b + d + f + h} = r = \dfrac{a}{b}.$ Ax. 4

$\therefore a + c + e + g : b + d + f + h = a : b$, by § 257.   Q. E. D.

PROPOSITION VII. THEOREM

270. *Like powers of the terms of a proportion are in proportion.*

Given $a : b = c : d.$

To prove that $a^n : b^n = c^n : d^n.$

Proof. $$\frac{a}{b} = \frac{c}{d}.$$ § 257

$$\therefore \frac{a^n}{b^n} = \frac{c^n}{d^n}, \text{ by Ax. 5.}$$ Q.E.D.

PROPOSITION VIII. THEOREM

271. *If three quantities are in continued proportion, the first is to the third as the square of the first is to the square of the second.*

Given $a : b = b : c.$

To prove that $a : c = a^2 : b^2.$

Proof. $a^2 = a^2,$ Iden.

and $ac = b^2.$ § 261

$$\therefore \frac{a^2}{ac} \text{ or } \frac{a}{c} = \frac{a^2}{b^2}.$$ Ax. 4

$$\therefore a : c = a^2 : b^2, \text{ by § 257.}$$ Q.E.D.

272. Nature of the Quantities in a Proportion. Although we may have ratios of lines, or of areas, or of solids, or of angles, we treat all of the terms of a proportion as *numbers*.

If b and d are lines or solids, for example, we cannot multiply each member of $\frac{a}{b} = \frac{c}{d}$ by bd, as in § 261.

Hence *when we speak of the product of two geometric magnitudes, we mean the product of the numbers that represent them when expressed in terms of a common unit.*

EXERCISE 42

1. Prove that $a : b = ma : mb$.

2. If $a : b = c : d$, and $m : n = p : q$, prove that $am : bn = cp : dq$.

If $a : b = c : d$, prove the following:

3. $a : d = bc : d^2$.

4. $1 : b = c : ad$.

5. $ad : b = c : 1$.

6. $ma : b = mc : d$.

7. $ma : nb = mc : nd$.

8. $a - 1 : b = bc - d : bd$.

9. $a + 1 : 1 = bc + d : d$.

10. $1 : bc = 1 : ad$.

11. $a + b : a - b = c + d : c - d$.

In Ex. 11, use § 267 and § 268, and Ax. 4. In this case a, b, c, and d are said to be in proportion *by composition and division*.

If $a : b = b : c$, prove the following:

12. $c : b = b : a$.

13. $a : c = b^2 : c^2$.

14. $\left(b + \sqrt{ac}\right)\left(b - \sqrt{ac}\right) = 0$.

15. $ac - 1 : b - 1 = b + 1 : 1$.

16. If $2 : 7 = 3 : x$, show that $2x = 21$, and $x = 10\frac{1}{2}$.

Find the value of x in the following:

17. $1 : 7 = 3 : x$.

18. $2 : 9 = 5 : x$.

19. $4 : 28 = 3 : x$.

20. $2 : 8 = x : 12$.

21. $3 : 5 = x : 9$.

22. $7 : 21 = x : 5$.

23. $3 : 5 = x + 1 : 10$.

24. $8 : 15 = 2x + 3 : 45$.

25. $0.8 : x = 4 : 9$.

26. $0.7 : x = 21 : 15$.

27. $0.25 : x = 5 : 8$.

28. $x : 1.3 = 4 : 0.26$.

29. $x : 2.7 = 7 : 5.4$.

30. $x : 8.1 = 0.3 : 0.9$.

31. $2 : x = x : 32$.

32. $7 : x = x : 28$.

33. $1 : 1 + x = x - 1 : 3$.

34. $5 : x - 2 = x + 2 : 1$.

35. $x^2 : 2a = 3a : 6$.

36. $x : 4a = 2a^2 : x^2$.

37. $a : 1 = x - 1 : 7$.

38. $x + 1 : x - 1 = 3 : 2$.

39. $3 : x + 4 = x - 4 : 3$.

40. $ab : b = b - cx : bc - x$.

PROPOSITION IX. THEOREM

273. *If a line is drawn through two sides of a triangle parallel to the third side, it divides the two sides proportionally.*

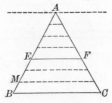

Given the triangle *ABC*, with *EF* drawn parallel to *BC*.

To prove that $EB : AE = FC : AF.$

CASE 1. *When AE and EB are commensurable.*

Proof. Assume that *MB* is a common measure of *AE* and *EB*. Let *MB* be contained *m* times in *EB*, and *n* times in *AE*.

Then $EB : AE = m : n.$

(For m and n are the numerical measures of EB and AE.)

At the points of division on *EB* and *AE* draw lines ∥ to *BC*. These lines will divide *AC* into $m + n$ equal parts, of which *FC* will contain *m* parts, and *AF* will contain *n* parts.   § 134

$$\therefore FC : AF = m : n.$$

$$\therefore EB : AE = FC : AF, \text{ by Ax. 8.}$$ Q. E. D.

For practical purposes this proves the proposition, for even if *AE* and *EB* are incommensurable, we can, by taking a unit of measure small enough, find the measure of *AE* and *EB* to as close a degree of approximation as we may desire, just as we can carry $\sqrt{2}$ to as many decimal places as we wish, although its exact value cannot be expressed rationally.

On this account many teachers omit the incommensurable case discussed on page 158, or merely require the proof there given to be read aloud and explained by the class.

CASE 2. *When AE and EB are incommensurable.*

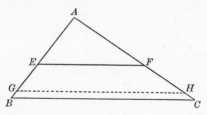

Proof. Divide AE into a number of equal parts, and apply one of these parts to EB as many times as EB will contain it.

Since AE and EB are incommensurable, a certain number of these parts will extend from E to some point G, leaving a remainder GB less than one of these parts.

Draw $GH \parallel$ to BC.

Then $EG : AE = FH : AF.$ Case 1

By increasing the *number* of equal parts into which AE is divided, we can make the *length* of each part less than any assigned positive value, however small, but not zero.

Hence GB, which is less than one of these equal parts, has zero for a limit.   § 204

And the corresponding segment HC has zero for a limit.

Therefore EG approaches EB as a limit,

            and FH approaches FC as a limit.

$\therefore$ the variable $\dfrac{EG}{AE}$ approaches $\dfrac{EB}{AE}$ as a limit,

and the variable $\dfrac{FH}{AF}$ approaches $\dfrac{FC}{AF}$ as a limit.

But $\dfrac{EG}{AE}$ is always equal to $\dfrac{FH}{AF}$.   Case 1

$\therefore \dfrac{EB}{AE} = \dfrac{FC}{AF}$, by § 207.   Q.E.D.

274. Corollary 1. *One side of a triangle is to either of its segments cut off by a line parallel to the base as the third side is to its corresponding segment.*

For $EB : AE = FC : AF.$ § 273

By composition, $EB + AE : AE = FC + AF : AF,$ § 267

or $AB : AE = AC : AF.$ Ax. 11

275. Corollary 2. *Three or more parallel lines cut off proportional intercepts on any two transversals.*

Draw $AN \parallel$ to CD.

Then $AL = CG$, $LM = GK$, $MN = KD$.   § 127

Now $AH : AM = AF : AL = FH : LM$, § 274

and $AH : AM = HB : MN.$ § 273

∴ $AF : CG = FH : GK = HB : KD.$ Ax. 9

EXERCISE 43

1. In the figure of § 275, suppose $AH = 5$ in., $AF = 2$ in., and $CK = 6$ in. Find the length of CG.

2. In this square PQ is $\parallel$ to AB. If a side of the square is 10 in., $DB = 14.14$ in. If $DP = 3$ in., what is the length of DQ?

3. The sides of a triangle are respectively 3 in., 4 in., and 5 in. A line is drawn parallel to the 4-inch side, cutting the 3-inch side 1 in. from the vertex of the largest angle. Find the length of the two segments cut from the longest side.

4. Two pieces of timber 1 ft. wide are fitted together at right angles as here shown. AB is 8 ft. long, AC 6 ft. long, and the distance BC, along the dotted line, is 10 ft. A carpenter finds it necessary to saw along the dotted line. Find the length of the slanting cut across the upright piece; across the horizontal piece.

Proposition X. Theorem

276. *If a line divides two sides of a triangle proportionally from the vertex, it is parallel to the third side.*

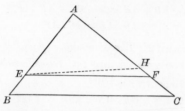

Given the triangle *ABC* with *EF* drawn so that

$$\frac{EB}{AE} = \frac{FC}{AF}.$$

To prove that   *EF is* ∥ *to BC*.

Proof. Suppose that *EF* is not parallel to *BC*.

Then from *E* draw some other line, as *EH*, parallel to *BC*.

Then $AB : AE = AC : AH.$ § 274

(One side of a △ is to either of its segments cut off by a line ∥ to the base as the third side is to its corresponding segment.)

But $EB : AE = FC : AF.$ Given

$\therefore EB + AE : AE = FC + AF : AF,$ § 267

or $AB : AE = AC : AF.$ Ax. 11

$\therefore AC : AF = AC : AH.$ Ax. 8

$\therefore AF = AH.$ § 263

(For the two antecedents are equal.)

$\therefore EF$ and *EH* must coincide.   Post. 1

(For their end points coincide.)

But   *EH* is ∥ to *BC*.   Const.

$\therefore EF$, which coincides with *EH*, is ∥ to *BC*.   Q.E.D.

This proposition is the converse of Prop. IX.

277. Dividing a Line into Segments. If a given line AB is divided at P, a point between the extremities A and B, it is said to be *divided internally* into the segments AP and PB; and if it is divided at P', a point in the prolongation of BA, it is said to be *divided externally* into the segments AP' and $P'B$.

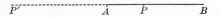

In either case the length of the segment is the *distance* from the point of division to an extremity of the line. If the line is divided internally, the *sum* of the segments is equal to the line; and if the line is divided externally, the *difference* of the segments is equal to the line.

Suppose it is required to divide the given line AB *internally and externally* in the same ratio; as, for example, in the ratio of the two numbers 3 and 5.

We divide AB into $3+5$, or 8, equal parts, and take 3 parts from A; we then have the point P, such that

$$AP : PB = 3 : 5. \tag{1}$$

Secondly, we divide AB into $5-3$, or 2, equal parts, and lay off on the prolongation of BA three of these equal parts; we then have the point P', such that

$$AP' : P'B = 3 : 5. \tag{2}$$

Comparing (1) and (2), we have

$$AP : PB = AP' : P'B.$$

278. Harmonic Division. If a given straight line is divided internally and externally into segments having the same ratio, the line is said to be *divided harmonically.*

Thus the line AB has just been divided internally and externally in the same ratio, 3 : 5, and AB is therefore said to be divided harmonically at P and P' in the ratio 3 : 5.

Proposition XI. Theorem

279. *The bisector of an angle of a triangle divides the opposite side into segments which are proportional to the adjacent sides.*

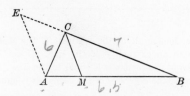

Given the bisector of the angle C of the triangle ABC, meeting AB at M.

To prove that $AM : MB = CA : CB$.

Proof. From A draw a line ∥ to MC.

This line must meet BC produced, because BC and MC cannot both be parallel to the same line.   § 94

Let this line meet BC produced at E.

Then $AM : MB = EC : CB$.   § 273

(If a line is drawn through two sides of a △ parallel to the third side, it divides the two sides proportionally.)

Also $\angle ACM = \angle CAE$,   § 100

(Alt.-int. ∠s of ∥ lines are equal.)

and $\angle MCB = \angle AEC$.   § 102

(Ext.-int. ∠s of ∥ lines are equal.)

But $\angle ACM = \angle MCB$.   Given

∴ $\angle CAE = \angle AEC$.   Ax. 8

∴ $EC = CA$.   § 76

Put CA for its equal EC in the first proportion.

Then $AM : MB = CA : CB$, by Ax. 9.   Q.E.D.

Proposition XII. Theorem

280. *The bisector of an exterior angle of a triangle divides the opposite side externally into segments which are proportional to the adjacent sides.*

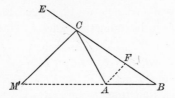

Given the bisector of the exterior angle *ECA* of the triangle *ABC*, meeting *BA* produced at *M'*.

To prove that $AM' : M'B = CA : CB.$

Proof. Draw *AF* ∥ to *M'C*, meeting *BC* at *F*.

Then $AM' : M'B = FC : CB.$ § 274

(*One side of a △ is to either of its segments cut off by a line ∥ to the base as the third side is to its corresponding segment.*)

Now $\angle ECM' = \angle CFA,$ § 102

and $\angle M'CA = \angle FAC.$ § 100

But $\angle ECM' = \angle M'CA.$ Given

∴ $\angle CFA = \angle FAC.$ Ax. 8

∴ $CA = FC.$ § 76

Put *CA* for its equal *FC* in the first proportion.

Then $AM' : M'B = CA : CB,$ by Ax. 9.   q.e.d.

Discussion. In case $CA = CB$, what is the arrangement of the lines?

281. Corollary. *The bisectors of the interior angle and the exterior angle at the same vertex of a triangle, meeting the opposite side, divide that side harmonically.*

EXERCISE 44

1. In a triangle ABC, $AB = 6.5$, $CA = 6$, $BC = 7$. Find the segments of AB made by the bisector of the angle C.

2. In a triangle ABC, $CA = 7.5$, $BC = 7$, $AB = 8$. Find the segments of CA made by the bisector of the angle B.

3. The sides of a triangle are 12, 16, 20. Find the segments of the sides made by bisecting the angles.

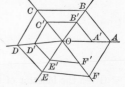

4. If a spider, in making its web, makes $A'B'$ ∥ to AB, $B'C'$ ∥ to BC, $C'D'$ ∥ to CD, $D'E'$ ∥ to DE, and $E'F'$ ∥ to EF, and then runs a line from F' ∥ to FA, will it strike the point A'? Prove it.

5. From any point O within the triangle ABC the lines OA, OB, OC are drawn and are bisected respectively by A', B', and C'. Prove that $\angle CBA = \angle C'B'A'$.

6. Prove Ex. 5 if the point O is outside the triangle.

7. From any point O within the quadrilateral $ABCD$ lines are drawn to the vertices A, B, C, D, and are bisected by A', B', C', D'. Prove that $\angle CBA = \angle C'B'A'$.

8. If a pendulum swings at the point O, cutting two parallel lines at P and Q respectively, the ratio $OP : OQ$ is constant.

9. Through a fixed point P a line is drawn cutting a fixed line at X. PX is then divided at Y so that the ratio $PY : YX$ is constant. Find the locus of the point Y as X moves along the fixed line.

10. From the point P on the side CA of the triangle ABC parallels to the other sides are drawn meeting AB in Q and BC in R. Prove that $AQ : QB = BR : RC$.

11. In the triangle ABC, P and Q are taken on the sides CA and BC so that $AP : PC = BQ : QC$. AR is then drawn parallel to PB, meeting CB produced in R. Prove that CB is the mean proportional between CQ and CR.

282. Similar Polygons. Polygons that have their corresponding angles equal, and their corresponding sides proportional, are called *similar polygons*.

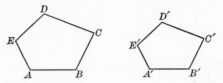

Thus the polygons $ABCDE$ and $A'B'C'D'E'$ are similar, if the ∠ A, B, C, D, E are equal respectively to the ∠ A', B', C', D', E', and if

$$AB : A'B' = BC : B'C' = CD : C'D' = DE : D'E' = EA : E'A'.$$

Similar polygons are commonly said to be of the same shape.

283. Corresponding Lines. In similar polygons those lines that are similarly situated with respect to the equal angles are called *corresponding lines*.

Corresponding lines are also called *homologous lines*.

284. Ratio of Similitude. The ratio of any two corresponding lines in similar polygons is called the *ratio of similitude* of the polygons.

The primary idea of similarity is likeness of form. The two conditions necessary for similarity are :

1. *For every angle in one of the figures there must be an equal angle in the other.*

2. *The corresponding sides must be proportional.*

Thus Q and Q' are not similar; the corresponding sides are proportional, but the corresponding angles are not equal. Also R and R' are not similar; the corresponding angles are equal, but the corresponding sides are not proportional.

In the case of *triangles* either condition implies the other.

PROPOSITION XIII. THEOREM

285. *Two mutually equiangular triangles are similar.*

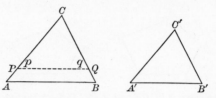

Given the triangles ABC and $A'B'C'$, having the angles A, B, C equal to the angles A', B', C' respectively.

To prove that the $\triangle ABC$ and $A'B'C'$ are similar.

Proof. Since the $\triangle$ are mutually equiangular,   Given

we have only to prove that

$$AB : A'B' = AC : A'C' = BC : B'C'. \qquad § 282$$

Place the $\triangle A'B'C'$ on the $\triangle ABC$ so that $\angle C'$ shall coincide with its equal, the $\angle C$, and $A'B'$ take the position PQ.   Post. 5

Then $\angle p = \angle A$.   Given

$\therefore PQ$ is $\parallel$ to AB.   § 103

$\therefore AC : PC = BC : QC;$ § 274

that is, $AC : A'C' = BC : B'C'.$ Ax. 9

Similarly, by placing the $\triangle A'B'C'$ on the $\triangle ABC$ so that $\angle B'$ shall coincide with its equal, the $\angle B$, we can prove that

$$AB : A'B' = BC : B'C'.$$

$\therefore AB : A'B' = AC : A'C' = BC : B'C'.$ Ax. 8

$\therefore \triangle ABC$ is similar to $\triangle A'B'C'$, by § 282.   Q. E. D.

286. COROLLARY 1. *Two triangles are similar if two angles of the one are equal respectively to two angles of the other.*

287. COROLLARY 2. *Two right triangles are similar if an acute angle of the one is equal to an acute angle of the other.*

Proposition XIV. Theorem

288. *If two triangles have an angle of the one equal to an angle of the other, and the including sides proportional, they are similar.*

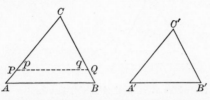

Given the triangles ABC and $A'B'C'$, with the angle C equal to the angle C' and with $CA : C'A' = CB : C'B'$.

To prove that the △ ABC and $A'B'C'$ are similar.

Proof. Place the △ $A'B'C'$ on the △ ABC so that $\angle C'$ shall coincide with its equal, the $\angle C$.   Post. 5

Then let △$A'B'C'$ take the position of the △PQC.

Now $$\frac{CA}{C'A'} = \frac{CB}{C'B'};$$ Given

that is, $$\frac{CA}{CP} = \frac{CB}{CQ}.$$ Ax. 9

$$\therefore \frac{CA - CP}{CP} = \frac{CB - CQ}{CQ},$$ § 268

or $$\frac{PA}{CP} = \frac{QB}{CQ}.$$

$\therefore PQ$ is ∥ to AB.   § 276

(If a line divides two sides of a △ proportionally, it is ∥ to the third side.)

$\therefore \angle p = \angle A$, and $\angle q = \angle B$.   § 102

Now $\angle C = \angle C'$.   Given

$\therefore$ △ PQC is similar to △ ABC.   § 285

$\therefore$ △ $A'B'C'$ is similar to △ ABC.   **Q. E. D.**

PROPOSITION XV. THEOREM

289. *If two triangles have their sides respectively proportional, they are similar.*

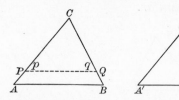

Given the triangles *ABC* and *A'B'C'*, having

$$AB : A'B' = BC : B'C' = CA : C'A'.$$

To prove that the △ ABC and A'B'C' are similar.

Proof. Upon *CA* take *CP* equal to *C'A'*, and upon *CB* take *CQ* equal to *C'B'*; and draw *PQ*.

Now $CA : C'A' = BC : B'C'.$ Given

Or, since $CP = C'A'$, and $CQ = C'B'$,   Const.

                    $CA : CP = CB : CQ.$ Ax. 9

Also $\angle C = \angle C.$ Iden.

∴ △ *ABC* and *PQC* are similar.   § 288

(If two △ have an angle of the one equal to an angle of the other, and the including sides proportional, they are similar.)

                    ∴ $CA : CP = AB : PQ$;   § 282

that is, $CA : C'A' = AB : PQ.$ Ax. 9

But $CA : C'A' = AB : A'B'.$ Given

                    ∴ $AB : PQ = AB : A'B'.$ Ax. 8

                    ∴ $PQ = A'B'.$ § 263

Hence the △ *PQC* and *A'B'C'* are congruent.   § 80

But   △ *PQC* has been proved similar to △ *ABC*.

                    ∴ △ *A'B'C'* is similar to △ *ABC*.   Q.E.D.

Proposition XVI. Theorem

290. *Two triangles which have their sides respectively parallel, or respectively perpendicular, are similar.*

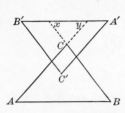 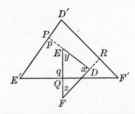

Given the triangles *ABC* and *A'B'C'*, with their sides respectively parallel; and the triangles *DEF* and *D'E'F'*, with their sides respectively perpendicular.

To prove that   1. *the △ ABC and A'B'C' are similar ;*
                     2. *the △ DEF and D'E'F' are similar.*

Proof. 1. Produce *BC* and *AC* to *B'A'*, forming ∠s x and y.

Then $\angle B = \angle x$ (§ 100), and $\angle B' = \angle x$.   § 102

              ∴ $\angle B = \angle B'$.   Ax. 8

In like manner, $\angle A = \angle A'$.

       ∴ △ *ABC* is similar to △ *A'B'C'*.   § 286

2. Produce *DE* and *FD* to meet *D'E'* and *F'D'* at *P* and *R*.

The quadrilateral *E'QEP* has ∠s p and q right angles. Given

       ∴ ∠s *E'* and *PEQ* are supplementary.   § 144

But   ∠s y and *PEQ* are supplementary.   § 43

Therefore $\angle y = \angle E'$.   § 58

In like manner, $\angle x = \angle D'$.

      ∴ △ *DEF* is similar to △ *D'E'F'*, by § 286.   Q. E. D.

Discussion. The parallel sides and the perpendicular sides respectively are corresponding sides of the triangles.

Proposition XVII. Theorem

291. *The perimeters of two similar polygons have the same ratio as any two corresponding sides.*

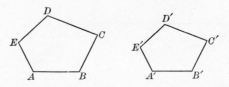

Given the two similar polygons *ABCDE* and *A'B'C'D'E'*, with *p* and *p'* representing their respective perimeters.

To prove that $p : p' = AB : A'B'.$

Proof.
$$\frac{AB}{A'B'} = \frac{BC}{B'C'} = \frac{CD}{C'D'} = \frac{DE}{D'E'} = \frac{EA}{E'A'}. \qquad \text{§ 282}$$

$$\therefore \frac{AB + BC + CD + DE + EA}{A'B' + B'C' + C'D' + D'E' + E'A'} = \frac{AB}{A'B'}. \qquad \text{§ 269}$$

$$\therefore p : p' = AB : A'B', \text{ by Ax. 9.} \qquad \text{Q.E.D.}$$

EXERCISE 45

1. The corresponding altitudes of two similar triangles have the same ratio as any two corresponding sides.

2. The base and altitude of a triangle are 15 in. and 7 in. respectively. The corresponding base of a similar triangle is 3.75 in. Find the corresponding altitude.

3. If two parallels are cut by three concurrent transversals, the corresponding segments of the parallels are proportional.

4. The point *P* is any point on the side *OX* of the angle *XOY*. From *P* a perpendicular *PQ* is let fall on *OY*. Prove that for any position of *P* on *OX* the ratio *OP* : *PQ* is constant, and the ratio *PQ* : *OQ* is constant.

75 : 60 :: 1 : x .

5. In drawing a map of a triangular field with sides 75 rd., 60 rd., and 50 rd. respectively, the longest side is drawn 1 in. long. How long are the other two sides drawn?

6. This figure represents part of a diagonal scale used by draftsmen. The distance from 0 to 10 is 1 centimeter, or 10 millimeters. Show how to measure 5 mm.; 1 mm.; 0.9 mm.; 0.5 mm.; 1.5 mm. On what proposition does this depend?

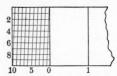

7. This figure represents a pair of proportional compasses used by draftsmen. By adjusting the screw at O, the lengths OA and OC, and the corresponding lengths OB and OD, may be varied proportionally. Prove that $\triangle OAB$ is always similar to $\triangle OCD$. If $OA = 3$ in. and $OC = 5$ in., then AB is what part of CD?

8. $ABCD$ is any polygon and P is any point. On AP any point A' is taken and $A'B'$ is drawn parallel to AB as shown. Then $B'C'$ and $C'D'$ are drawn parallel to BC and CD. Is $D'A'$ parallel to DA? Is $A'B'C'D'$ similar to $ABCD$? Prove it.

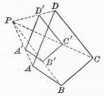

9. If two circles are tangent externally, the corresponding segments of two lines drawn through the point of contact and terminated by the circles are proportional.

10. If two circles are tangent externally, their common external tangent is the mean proportional between their diameters.

11. AB and AC are chords drawn from any point A on a circle, and AD is a diameter. If the tangent at D intersects AB and AC at E and F, the triangles ABC and AEF are similar.

12. If AD and BE are two altitudes of the triangle ABC, the triangles DEC and ABC are similar.

Proposition XVIII. Theorem

292. *If two polygons are similar, they can be separated into the same number of triangles, similar each to each, and similarly placed.*

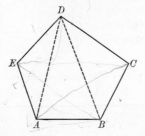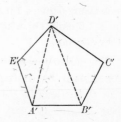

Given two similar polygons *ABCDE* and *A'B'C'D'E'* with angles *A*, *B*, *C*, *D*, *E* equal to angles *A'*, *B'*, *C'*, *D'*, *E'* respectively.

To prove that ABCDE and A'B'C'D'E' can be separated into the same number of triangles, similar each to each, and similarly placed.

Proof. Draw the corresponding diagonals *DA*, *D'A'*, and *DB*, *D'B'*.

	Since $\angle E = \angle E'$,	§ 282
and	$DE : D'E' = EA : E'A'$,	§ 282
	∴ △ *DEA* and *D'E'A'* are similar.	§ 288

In like manner, △ *DBC* and *D'B'C'* are similar.

Furthermore	$\angle BAE = \angle B'A'E'$,	§ 282
and	$\angle DAE = \angle D'A'E'$.	§ 282
By subtracting,	$\angle BAD = \angle B'A'D'$.	Ax. 2
Now	$DA : D'A' = EA : E'A'$,	§ 282
and	$AB : A'B' = EA : E'A'$.	§ 282
	∴ $DA : D'A' = AB : A'B'$.	Ax. 8

∴ △ *DAB* and *D'A'B'* are similar, by § 288.   **Q.E.D.**

PROPOSITION XIX. THEOREM

293. *If two polygons are composed of the same number of triangles, similar each to each, and similarly placed, the polygons are similar.*

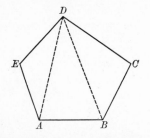 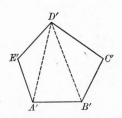

Given two polygons $ABCDE$ and $A'B'C'D'E'$ composed of the triangles DEA, DAB, DBC, similar respectively to the triangles $D'E'A'$, $D'A'B'$, $D'B'C'$, and similarly placed.

To prove that $ABCDE$ is similar to $A'B'C'D'E'$.

Proof.	$\angle E = \angle E'$.	§ 282
Also	$\angle DAE = \angle D'A'E'$,	
and	$\angle BAD = \angle B'A'D'$.	§ 282
By adding,	$\angle BAE = \angle B'A'E'$.	Ax. 1

Similarly $\angle CBA = \angle C'B'A'$, and $\angle EDC = \angle E'D'C'$.

Again, $\angle C = \angle C'$.   § 282

Hence the polygons are mutually equiangular.

Also $\dfrac{DE}{D'E'} = \dfrac{EA}{E'A'} = \dfrac{DA}{D'A'} = \dfrac{AB}{A'B'} = \dfrac{DB}{D'B'} = \dfrac{BC}{B'C'} = \dfrac{CD}{C'D'}$. § 282

Hence the polygons are not only mutually equiangular but they have their corresponding sides proportional.

Therefore the polygons are similar, by § 282.   Q.E.D.

This proposition is the converse of Prop. XVIII.

Proposition XX. Theorem

294. *If in a right triangle a perpendicular is drawn from the vertex of the right angle to the hypotenuse:*

1. *The triangles thus formed are similar to the given triangle, and are similar to each other.*

2. *The perpendicular is the mean proportional between the segments of the hypotenuse.*

3. *Each of the other sides is the mean proportional between the hypotenuse and the segment of the hypotenuse adjacent to that side.*

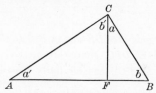

Given the right triangle *ABC*, with *CF* drawn from the vertex of the right angle *C*, perpendicular to *AB*.

1. *To prove that the △ BCA, CFA, BFC are similar.*

Proof. Since the ∠ *a′* is common to the rt. △ *CFA* and *BCA*,

∴ these △ are similar. § 287

Since the ∠ *b* is common to the rt. △ *BFC* and *BCA*,

∴ these △ are similar. § 287

Since the △ *CFA* and *BFC* are each similar to △ *BCA*,

∴ these △ are mutually equiangular. § 282

Therefore the △ *CFA* and *BFC* are similar, by § 285. Q.E.D.

2. *To prove that* $AF : CF = CF : FB$.

Proof. In the similar △ *CFA* and *BFC*,

$$AF : CF = CF : FB, \text{ by § 282.}$$ Q.E.D.

3. *To prove that* $AB : AC = AC : AF$,

and $AB : BC = BC : BF$.

Proof. In the similar $\triangle$ *BCA* and *CFA*,

$$AB : AC = AC : AF.$$ § 282

In the similar $\triangle$ *BCA* and *BFC*,

$$AB : BC = BC : BF, \text{ by § 282.}$$ Q.E.D.

295. COROLLARY 1. *The squares on the two sides of a right triangle are proportional to the segments of the hypotenuse adjacent to those sides.*

From the proportions in § 294, 3,

$$\overline{AC}^2 = AB \times AF, \text{ and } \overline{BC}^2 = AB \times BF.$$ § 261

Hence $$\frac{\overline{AC}^2}{\overline{BC}^2} = \frac{AB \times AF}{AB \times BF} = \frac{AF}{BF}.$$ Ax. 4

296. COROLLARY 2. *The square on the hypotenuse and the square on either side of a right triangle are proportional to the hypotenuse and the segment of the hypotenuse adjacent to that side.*

Since $$\overline{AB}^2 = AB \times AB,$$ Iden.

and, as in § 295, $$\overline{AC}^2 = AB \times AF,$$ § 261

$$\therefore \frac{\overline{AB}^2}{\overline{AC}^2} = \frac{AB \times AB}{AB \times AF} = \frac{AB}{AF}.$$ Ax. 4

297. COROLLARY 3. *The perpendicular from any point on a circle to a diameter is the mean proportional between the segments of the diameter.*

298. COROLLARY 4. *If a perpendicular is drawn from any point on a circle to a diameter, the chord from that point to either extremity of the diameter is the mean proportional between the diameter and the segment adjacent to that chord.*

EXERCISE 46

1. The perimeters of two similar polygons are 18 in. and 14 in. If a side of the first is 3 in., find the corresponding side of the second.

2. In two similar triangles, ABC and $A'B'C'$, $AB = 6$ in., $BC = 7$ in., $CA = 8$ in., and $A'B' = 9$ in. Find $B'C'$ and $C'A'$.

3. The corresponding bases of two similar triangles are 11 in. and 13 in. The altitude of the first is 6 in. Find the corresponding altitude of the second.

4. The perimeter of an equilateral triangle is 51 in. Find the side of an equilateral triangle of half the altitude.

5. The sides of a polygon are 2 in., $2\frac{1}{2}$ in., $3\frac{1}{4}$ in., 3 in., and 5 in. Find the perimeter of a similar polygon whose longest side is 7 in.

6. The perimeter of an isosceles triangle is 13, and the ratio of one of the equal sides to the base is $1\frac{2}{3}$. Find the three sides.

7. The perimeter of a rectangle is 48 in., and the ratio of two of the sides is $\frac{5}{7}$. Find the sides.

8. In drawing a map to the scale $\frac{1}{100000}$, what length will represent the sides of a county that is a rectangle 25 mi. long and 10 mi. wide ? Answer to the nearest tenth of an inch.

9. Two circles touch at P. Through P three lines are drawn, meeting one circle in A, B, C, and the other in A', B', C' respectively. Prove the triangles ABC, $A'B'C'$ similar.

10. If two circles are tangent internally, all chords of the greater circle drawn from the point of contact are divided proportionally by the smaller circle.

11. In an inscribed quadrilateral the product of the diagonals is equal to the sum of the products of the opposite sides.

Draw DE, making $\angle EDC = \angle ADB$. The $\triangle ABD$ and ECD are similar ; and the $\triangle BCD$ and AED are similar.

PROPOSITION XXI.   THEOREM

299. *If two chords intersect within a circle, the product of the segments of the one is equal to the product of the segments of the other.*

Given the chords *AB* and *CD*, intersecting at *P*.

To prove that $PA \times PB = PC \times PD.$

Proof.   Draw *AC* and *BD*.

Then   since $\angle a = \angle a'$,   § 214

(*Each is measured by $\frac{1}{2}$ arc CB.*)

and $\angle c = \angle c'$,   § 214

(*Each is measured by $\frac{1}{2}$ arc DA.*)

∴ the △ *CPA* and *BPD* are similar.   § 286

∴ $PA : PD = PC : PB.$ § 282

∴ $PA \times PB = PC \times PD$, by § 261.   Q.E.D.

300. COROLLARY. *If two chords intersect within a circle, the segments of the one are reciprocally proportional to the segments of the other.*

This means, for example, that *PA* : *PD* equals the *reciprocal* of *PB* : *PC*, or equals *PC* : *PB*, as shown above.

301. Secant to a Circle. *A secant from an external point to a circle* is understood to mean the segment of the secant that lies between the given external point and the *second point* of intersection of the secant and circle.

Proposition XXII. Theorem

302. *If from a point outside a circle a secant and a tangent are drawn, the tangent is the mean proportional between the secant and its external segment.*

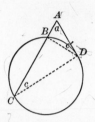

Given a tangent AD and a secant AC drawn from the point A to the circle BCD.

To prove that $AC : AD = AD : AB.$

Proof.   Draw DC and DB.

Now $\angle c$ is measured by $\frac{1}{2}$ arc DB,   § 214

and $\angle c'$ is measured by $\frac{1}{2}$ arc DB.   § 220

$$\therefore \angle c = \angle c'.$$

Then in the $\triangle ADC$ and ABD,

$\angle a = \angle a$,   Iden.

and $\angle c = \angle c'$.

$\therefore \triangle ADC$ and ABD are similar.   § 286

$\therefore AC : AD = AD : AB$, by § 282.   Q.E.D.

303. **Corollary.** *If from a fixed point outside a circle a secant is drawn, the product of the secant and its external segment is constant in whatever direction the secant is drawn.*

Since $AC : AD = AD : AB,$ § 302

$$\therefore AC \times AB = \overline{AD}^2.$$ § 261

Since AD is constant (§ 192), therefore $AC \times AB$ is constant.

304. *The square on the bisector of an angle of a triangle is equal to the product of the sides of this angle diminished by the product of the segments made by the bisector upon the third side of the triangle.*

Given the line *CP* bisecting the angle *ACB* of the triangle *ABC*.

To prove that $\overline{CP}^2 = CA \times BC - AP \times PB.$

Proof. Circumscribe the ⊙ *BCA* about the △ *ABC*.   § 240

Produce *CP* to meet the circle in *D*, and draw *BD*.

Then in the △ *BCD* and *PCA*,

$$\angle m = \angle m', \qquad\qquad \text{Given}$$

and $\qquad\qquad \angle a' = \angle a. \qquad\qquad$ § 214

(Each is measured by ½ arc BC.)

∴ the △ *BCD* and *PCA* are similar.   § 286

∴ *CD* : *CA* = *BC* : *CP*.   § 282

∴ *CA* × *BC* = *CD* × *CP*   § 261

$$= (CP + PD) CP \qquad \text{Ax. 9}$$
$$= \overline{CP}^2 + CP \times PD.$$

But $\qquad\qquad CP \times PD = AP \times PB. \qquad$ § 299

∴ *CA* × *BC* = $\overline{CP}^2$ + *AP* × *PB*.   Ax. 9

∴ $\overline{CP}^2 = CA \times BC - AP \times PB$, by Ax. 2.   Q.E.D.

This theorem enables us to compute the bisectors of the angles of a triangle terminated by the opposite sides, if the sides are known. The theorem may be omitted without destroying the sequence.

Proposition XXIV. Theorem

305. *In any triangle the product of two sides is equal to the product of the diameter of the circumscribed circle by the altitude upon the third side.*

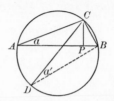

Given the triangle *ABC* with *CP* the altitude, *ADBC* the circle circumscribed about the triangle *ABC*, and *CD* a diameter.

To prove that $CA \times BC = CD \times CP.$

Proof.   Draw *BD*.

Then in the $\triangle$ *APC* and *DBC*,

$\angle CPA$ is a rt. $\angle$,	Given
$\angle CBD$ is a rt. $\angle$,	§ 215

$\angle a$ is measured by $\frac{1}{2}$ arc *BC*,

and $\angle a'$ is measured by $\frac{1}{2}$ arc *BC*.   § 214

$$\therefore \angle a = \angle a'.$$

$\therefore \triangle APC$ and *DBC* are similar.   § 287

(Two rt. $\triangle$ are similar if an acute $\angle$ of the one is equal to an acute $\angle$ of the other.)

$$\therefore CA : CD = CP : BC.$$ § 282

$\therefore CA \times BC = CD \times CP$, by § 261.   Q.E.D.

This theorem may be omitted without destroying the sequence. Props. XXIII and XXIV are occasionally demanded in college entrance examinations, but they are not necessary for proving subsequent propositions or for any of the exercises. Teachers may therefore use their judgment as to including them.

EXERCISE 47

1. The tangents to two intersecting circles, drawn from any point in their common chord produced, are equal.

2. The common chord of two intersecting circles, if produced, bisects their common tangents.

3. If two circles are tangent externally, the common internal tangent bisects the two common external tangents.

4. If a line drawn from a vertex of a triangle divides the opposite side into segments proportional to the adjacent sides, the line bisects the angle at the vertex.

5 If three circles intersect one another, the common chords are concurrent.

Let two of the chords, AB and CD, meet at O. Join the point of intersection E to O, and suppose that EO produced meets the same two circles at two different points P and Q. Then prove that $OP = OQ$ (§ 299), and hence that the points P and Q coincide.

6. The square on the bisector of an exterior angle of a triangle is equal to the product of the segments determined by this bisector upon the opposite side, diminished by the product of the other two sides.

Let CD bisect the exterior $\angle BCH$ of the $\triangle ABC$. $\triangle ADC$ and FBC are similar (§ 286). Apply § 303.

7. If the line of centers of two circles meets the circles at the consecutive points A, B, C, D, and meets the common external tangent at P, then $PA \times PD = PB \times PC$.

8. The line of centers of two circles meets the common external tangent at P, and a secant is drawn from P, cutting the circles at the consecutive points E, F, G, H. Prove that $PE \times PH = PF \times PG$.

Draw radii to the points of contact, and to E, F, G, H. Let fall ⊥s on PH from the centers of the ⊙. The various pairs of △ are similar.

Proposition XXV. Problem

306. *To divide a given line into parts proportional to any number of given lines.*

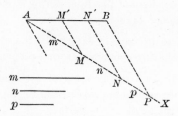

Given the lines *AB*, *m*, *n*, and *p*.

Required to divide AB into parts proportional to m, n, and p.

Construction.   Draw *AX*, making any convenient ∠ with *AB*.

On *AX* take *AM* equal to *m*,

MN equal to *n*, and *NP* equal to *p*.

Draw *BP*.

From *N* draw *NN'* ∥ to *PB*,

and from *M* draw *MM'* ∥ to *PB*.   § 233

Then   *M'* and *N'* are the division points required.   Q E F

Proof.   Through *A* draw a line ∥ to *PB*.   § 233

$$\frac{AM'}{AM} = \frac{M'N'}{MN} = \frac{N'B}{NP}.$$ § 275

(*Three or more* ∥ *lines cut off proportional intercepts on any two transversals.*)

Substituting *m*, *n*, and *p* for their equals *AM*, *MN*, and *NP*,

we have $$\frac{AM'}{m} = \frac{M'N'}{n} = \frac{N'B}{p}.$$ Ax. 9

This means that *AB* has been divided as required.   Q.E.D.

In like manner, we may divide *AB* into parts proportional to any number of given lines.

PROPOSITION XXVI. PROBLEM

307. *To find the fourth proportional to three given lines.*

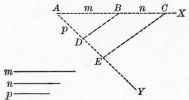

Given the three lines *m*, *n*, and *p*.

Required to find the fourth proportional to m, n, and p.

Construction. Draw two lines AX and AY containing any convenient angle.

On AX take AB equal to m,

and take BC equal to n.

On AY take AD equal to p.

Draw BD.

From C draw $CE \parallel$ to BD, meeting AY at E.   § 233

Then DE is the fourth proportional required.   Q.E.F.

Proof. $AB : BC = AD : DE.$ § 273

(If a line is drawn through two sides of a △ ∥ to the third side, it divides the two sides proportionally.)

Substituting m, n, and p for their equals AB, BC, and AD, we have $m : n = p : DE.$ Ax. 9

Therefore DE is the fourth proportional to m, n, and p, by § 259.   Q.E.D.

308. COROLLARY. *To find the third proportional to two given lines.*

In the above proof take m, n, n as the given lines instead of m, n, p.

Proposition XXVII. Problem

309. *To find the mean proportional between two given lines.*

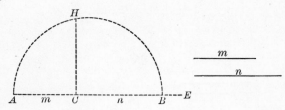

Given the two lines *m* and *n*.

Required to find the mean proportional between m and n.

Construction. Draw any line AE, and on AE take AC equal to *m*, and CB equal to *n*.

On AB as a diameter describe a semicircle.

At C erect the $\perp CH$, meeting the circle at H.   § 228

Then CH is the mean proportional between *m* and *n*.   Q.E.F.

Proof. $AC : CH = CH : CB.$ § 297

(The $\perp$ from any point on a circle to a diameter is the mean proportional between the segments of the diameter.)

Substituting for AC and CB their equals *m* and *n*,

we have $m : CH = CH : n$, by Ax. 9.   Q.E.D.

310. Extreme and Mean Ratio. If a line is divided into two segments such that one segment is the mean proportional between the whole line and the other segment, the line is said to be divided in *extreme and mean ratio*.

E.g. the line *a* is divided in extreme and mean ratio, if a segment *x* is found such that
$$a : x = x : a - x.$$

The division of a line in extreme and mean ratio is often called the *Golden Section.*

Proposition XXVIII. Problem

311. *To divide a given line in extreme and mean ratio.*

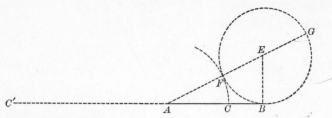

Given the line AB.

Required to divide AB in extreme and mean ratio.

Construction. At B erect a $\perp BE$ equal to half of AB.   § 228

From E as a center, with a radius equal to EB, describe a $\odot$.

Draw AE, meeting the circle at F and G.

On AB take AC equal to AF.

On BA produced take AC' equal to AG.

Then AB is divided internally at C and externally at C' in extreme and mean ratio.

That is, $AB : AC = AC : CB$, and $AB : AC' = AC' : C'B$.   q.e.f.

Proof. $AG : AB = AB : AF.$ § 302

From $AG : AB = AB : AF$,	$\therefore AB : AG = AF : AB.$ § 266
$AG - AB : AB =$	$\therefore AB + AG : AG =$
$\qquad AB - AF : AF.$	$\qquad AF + AB : AB.$
$\therefore AG - FG : AB =$	$\therefore AB + AC' : AC' =$
$\qquad AB - AC : AC.$	$\qquad AF + FG : AB.$
$\therefore AC : AB = CB : AC.$	$\therefore C'B : AC' = AC' : AB.$
$\therefore AB : AC = AC : CB,$	$\therefore AB : AC' = AC' : C'B,$
by inversion, § 266. q.e.d.	by §§ 261, 264. q.e.d.

Proposition XXIX. Problem

312. *Upon a given line corresponding to a given side of a given polygon, to construct a polygon similar to the given polygon.*

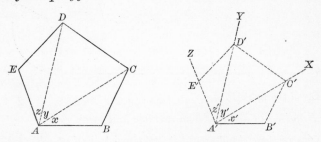

Given the line $A'B'$ and the polygon $ABCDE$.

Required to construct on $A'B'$, corresponding to AB, a polygon similar to the polygon $ABCDE$.

Construction. From A draw the diagonals AD and AC.

From A' draw $A'X$, $A'Y$, and $A'Z$, making $\measuredangle x'$, y', and z' equal respectively to $\measuredangle x$, y, and z.   § 232

From B' draw a line, making $\angle B'$ equal to $\angle B$,
                    and meeting $A'X$ at C'.

From C' draw a line, making $\angle D'C'B'$ equal to $\angle DCB$,
                    and meeting $A'Y$ at D'.

From D' draw a line, making $\angle E'D'C'$ equal to $\angle EDC$,
                    and meeting $A'Z$ at E'.

    Then $A'B'C'D'E'$ is the required polygon.   Q. E. F.

Proof. The $\triangle ABC$ and $A'B'C'$, the $\triangle ACD$ and $A'C'D'$, and the $\triangle ADE$ and $A'D'E'$, are similar.   § 286

    Therefore the two polygons are similar, by § 293.   Q. E. D.

EXERCISE 48

1. If a and b are two given lines, construct a line equal to x, where $x = \sqrt{ab}$. Consider the special case of $a = 2$, $b = 3$.

2. If m and n are two given lines, construct a line equal to x, where $x = \sqrt{2\,mn}$.

3. Determine both by geometric construction and arithmetically the third proportional to the lines $1\frac{1}{2}$ in. and 2 in.

4. Determine both by geometric construction and arithmetically the third proportional to the lines 4 in. and 3 in.

5. Determine both by geometric construction and arithmetically the fourth proportional to the lines $1\frac{1}{4}$ in., 2 in., and $2\frac{1}{4}$ in.

6. Determine both by geometric construction and arithmetically the mean proportional between the lines 1.2 in. and 2.7 in.

7. Find geometrically the square root of 5. Measure the line and thus determine the approximate arithmetical value.

8. A map is drawn to the scale of 1 in. to 50 mi. How far apart are two places that are $2\frac{3}{32}$ in. apart on the map?

9. Find by geometric construction and arithmetically the third proportional to the two lines $1\frac{3}{16}$ in. and $2\frac{5}{8}$ in.

10. Divide a line 1 in. long in extreme and mean ratio. Measure the two segments and determine their lengths to the nearest sixteenth of an inch.

11. Divide a line 5 in. long in extreme and mean ratio. Measure the two segments and determine their lengths to the nearest sixteenth of an inch.

12. Divide a line 6 in. long in extreme and mean ratio. Measure the two segments and determine their lengths to the nearest sixteenth of an inch.

The propositions on this page are taken from recent college entrance examination papers.

13. Through a given point P within a given circle to draw a chord AB so that the ratio $AP : BP$ shall equal a given ratio $m : n$.

Draw OPC so that $OP : PC = n : m$.
Draw CA equal to the fourth proportional to n, m, and the radius of the circle.

14. To draw two lines making an angle of 60°, and to construct all the circles of $\frac{1}{2}$ in. radius that are tangent to both lines.

15. To draw through a given point P in the arc subtended by a chord AB a chord which shall be bisected by AB.

On radius OP take CD equal to CP. Draw $DE \parallel$ to BA.

16. To construct two circles of radii $\frac{1}{2}$ in. and 1 in. respectively, which shall be tangent externally, and to construct a third circle of radius 3 in., which shall be tangent to each of these two circles and inclose both of them.

17. To draw through a given external point P a secant PAB to a given circle so that the ratio $PA : AB$ shall equal the given ratio $m : n$.

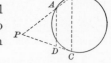

Draw the tangent PC. Make $PD : DC = m : n$. $PA : PC = PC : PB$.

18. To draw through a given external point P a secant PAB to a given circle so that $\overline{AB}^2 = PA \times PB$.

19. An equilateral triangle ABC is 2 in. on a side. To construct a circle which shall be tangent to AB at the point A and shall pass through the point C.

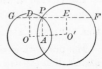

20. To draw through one of the points of intersection of two circles a secant so that the two chords that are formed shall be in the given ratio $m : n$.

21. In a circle of 3 in. radius chords are drawn through a point 1 in. from the center. What is the product of the segments of these chords?

22. The chord AB is 3 in. long, and it is produced through B to the point P so that PB is equal to 12 in. Find the tangent from P.

23. Two lines AB and CD intersect at O. How would you ascertain, by measuring OA, OB, OC, and OD, whether or not the four points A, B, C, and D lie on the same circle?

24. This figure represents an instrument for finding the centers of circular plates or sections of shafts. OC is a ruler that bisects the angle AOB, and AO and OB are equal. Show that, if A and B rest on the circle, OC passes through the center, and that by drawing two lines the center can be found.

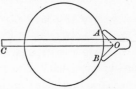

25. If three circles are tangent externally each to the other two, the tangents at their points of contact pass through the center of the circle inscribed in the triangle formed by joining the centers of the three given circles.

26. In the isosceles triangle ABC, C is a right angle, and AC is 4 in. With A as center and a radius 2 in. a circle is described. Required to describe another circle tangent to the first and also tangent to BC at the point B.

27. Find the center of a circle of $\frac{1}{2}$ in. radius, so drawn in a semicircle of radius 2 in. as to be tangent to the semicircle itself and to its diameter.

28. To inscribe in a given circle a triangle similar to a given triangle.

29. To draw two straight line-segments, having given their sum and their ratio.

EXERCISE 49

Review Questions

1. What is meant by ratio? by proportion?

2. If $a : b = c : d$, write four other proportions involving these quantities.

3. If $a : b = c : d$, is it true in general that $a + 1 : b + 1 = c : d$? Is it ever true?

4. When is a line divided harmonically? The bisectors of what angles of a triangle divide the opposite side harmonically?

5. What are the two conditions necessary for the similarity of two polygons?

6. Are two mutually equiangular triangles similar? Are two mutually equiangular polygons always similar?

7. Are two triangles similar if their corresponding sides are proportional? Are two polygons always similar if their corresponding sides are proportional?

8. If two triangles have their sides respectively parallel, are they similar? Is this true of polygons in general?

9. If two triangles have their sides respectively perpendicular, are they similar? Is this true of polygons in general?

10. Complete in two ways: The perimeters of two similar polygons have the same ratio as any two corresponding · · · ·.

11. If in a right triangle a perpendicular is drawn from the vertex of the right angle to the hypotenuse, state three geometric truths that follow.

12. If two secants intersect outside, on, or within a circle, what geometric truth follows?

13. How would you proceed to divide a straight line into seven equal parts?

14. How would you proceed to find the square root of 7 by measuring the length of a line?

BOOK IV

AREAS OF POLYGONS

313. Unit of Surface. A square the side of which is a unit of length is called a *unit of surface*.

Thus a square that is 1 inch long is 1 square inch, and a square that is 1 mile long is 1 square mile. If we are measuring the dimensions of a room in feet, we measure the surface of the floor in square feet. In the same way we may measure the page of this book in square inches and the area of a state in square miles.

314. Area of a Surface. The measure of a surface, expressed in units of surface, is called its *area*.

If a room is 20 feet long and 15 feet wide, the floor contains 300 square feet. Therefore the area of the floor is 300 square feet. Usually the two sides of a rectangle are not commensurable, although by means of fractions we may measure them to any required degree of approximation. The incommensurable cases in theorems like Prop. I of this Book may be omitted without interfering with the sequence of the course.

315. Equivalent Figures. Plane figures that have equal areas are said to be *equivalent*.

In propositions relating to areas the words *rectangle*, *triangle*, etc., are often used for *area of rectangle*, *area of triangle*, etc.

Since congruent figures may be made to coincide, congruent figures are manifestly equivalent.

Because their areas are equal, equivalent figures are frequently spoken of as equal figures. The symbol = is used both for "equivalent" and for "congruent," the sense determining which meaning is to be assigned to it. Occasionally these symbols are used : ≅, ≌, or ≡ for congruent, = for equal, and ∽ for equivalent.

Since the word *congruent* means "identically equal," the word *equal* is often used to mean "equivalent."

Proposition I. Theorem

316. *Two rectangles having equal altitudes are to each other as their bases.*

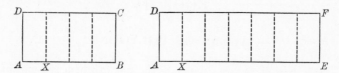

Given the rectangles *AC* and *AF*, having equal altitudes *AD*.

To prove that $\square\, AC : \square\, AF = base\ AB : base\ AE.$

Case 1. *When AB and AE are commensurable.*

Proof. Suppose AB and AE have a common measure, as AX. Suppose AX is contained m times in AB and n times in AE.

Then $\qquad\qquad\qquad AB : AE = m : n.$

(For m and n are the numerical measures of AB and AE.)

Apply AX as a unit of measure to AB and AE, and at the several points of division erect ⊥s.

These ⊥s are all ⊥ to the upper bases,   § 97

and   these ⊥s are all equal.   § 128

Since to each base equal to AX there is one rectangle,

$\therefore \square\, AC$ is divided into m rectangles,

and $\square\, AF$ is divided into n rectangles.   § 119

These rectangles are all congruent.   § 133

$\therefore \square\, AC : \square\, AF = m : n.$

$\therefore \square\, AC : \square\, AF = AB : AE$, by Ax. 8.   Q. E. D.

In this proposition we again meet the incommensurable case, as on pages 116 and 157. This case is considered on page 193 and may be omitted without destroying the sequence of the propositions.

CASE 2. *When AB and AE are incommensurable.*

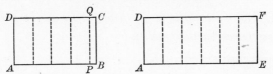

Proof. Divide AE into any number of equal parts, and apply one of these parts to AB as many times as AB will contain it.

Since AB and AE are incommensurable, a certain number of these parts will extend from A to some point P, leaving a remainder PB less than one of them. Draw $PQ \perp$ to AB.

Then $$\frac{\square\,AQ}{\square\,AF} = \frac{AP}{AE}.$$ Case 1

By increasing the *number* of equal parts into which AE is divided we can diminish the *length* of each, and therefore can make PB less than any assigned positive value, however small.

Hence PB approaches zero as a limit, as the number of parts of AE is indefinitely increased, and at the same time the corresponding $\square\,PC$ approaches zero as a limit.   § 204

Therefore AP approaches AB as a limit, and $\square\,AQ$ approaches $\square\,AC$ as a limit.

∴ the variable $\dfrac{AP}{AE}$ approaches $\dfrac{AB}{AE}$ as a limit,

and the variable $\dfrac{\square\,AQ}{\square\,AF}$ approaches $\dfrac{\square\,AC}{\square\,AF}$ as a limit.

But $\dfrac{AP}{AE}$ is always equal to $\dfrac{\square\,AQ}{\square\,AF}$, as AP varies in value and approaches AB as a limit.   Case 1

$$\therefore \frac{\square\,AC}{\square\,AF} = \frac{AB}{AE}, \text{ by § 207.}$$ Q.E.D.

317. COROLLARY. *Two rectangles having equal bases are to each other as their altitudes.*

Proposition II. Theorem

318. *Two rectangles are to each other as the products of their bases by their altitudes.*

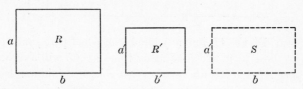

Given the rectangles R and R', having for the numerical measure of their bases b and b', and of their altitudes a and a' respectively.

To prove that $$\frac{R}{R'} = \frac{ab}{a'b'}.$$

Proof. Construct the rectangle S, with its base equal to that of R, and its altitude equal to that of R'.

Then $$\frac{R}{S} = \frac{a}{a'},$$ § 317

and $$\frac{S}{R'} = \frac{b}{b'}.$$ § 316

Since we are considering areas, we may treat R, R', and S as numbers and take the products of the corresponding members of these equations. § 272

We therefore have $\dfrac{R}{R'} = \dfrac{ab}{a'b'},$ by Ax. 3. Q.E.D.

319. Products of Lines. When we speak of the product of a and b we mean the product of their numerical values. It is possible, however, to think of a line as the product of two lines, by changing the definition of multiplication. Thus in this figure in which two parallels are cut by two intersecting transversals, we have $1 : a = b : x$. Therefore $x = ab$. In the same way we may find xc, or abc, the product of three lines.

PROPOSITION III.   THEOREM

320. *The area of a rectangle is equal to the product of its base by its altitude.*

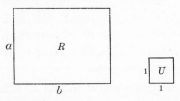

Given the rectangle *R*, having for the numerical measure of its base and altitude *b* and *a* respectively.

To prove that   *the area of R* = *ab.*

Proof. Let *U* be the unit of surface.   § 313

Then $$\frac{R}{U} = \frac{ab}{1 \times 1} = ab.$$ § 318

But $\frac{R}{U}$ = the *number* of units of surface in *R*, i.e. the area of *R*.   § 314

∴ the area of *R* = *ab*, by Ax. 8.   Q.E.D.

321. Practical Measures. When the base and altitude both contain the linear unit an integral number of times, this proposition is rendered evident by dividing the rectangle into squares, each equal to the unit of surface.

Thus, if the base contains seven linear units and the altitude four, the rectangle may be divided into twenty-eight squares, each equal to the unit of surface. Practically this is the way in which we conceive the measure of all rectangles. Even if the sides are incommensurable, we cannot determine this by any measuring instrument. If they seem to be incommensurable with a unit of a thousandth of an inch, they might not seem to be incommensurable with a unit of a millionth of an inch.

EXERCISE 50

1. A square and a rectangle have equal perimeters, **144** yd., and the length of the rectangle is five times the breadth. Compare the areas of the square and rectangle.

2. On a certain map the linear scale is 1 in. to 10 mi. How many acres are represented by a square ¾ in. on a side?

3. Find the ratio of a lot 90 ft. long by 60 ft. wide to a field 40 rd. long by 20 rd. wide.

4. Find the area of a gravel walk 3 ft. 6 in. wide, which surrounds a rectangular plot of grass 40 ft. long and 25 ft. wide. Make a drawing to scale before beginning to compute.

5. Find the number of square inches in this cross section of an L beam, the thickness being ⅓ in.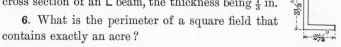

6. What is the perimeter of a square field that contains exactly an acre?

7. A machine for planing iron plates planes a space ½ in. wide and 18 ft. long in 1 min. How long will it take to plane a plate 22 ft. 6 in. long and 4 ft. 6 in. wide, allowing 51 min. for adjusting the machine?

8. How many tiles, each 8 in. square, will it take to cover a floor 24 ft. 8 in. long by 16 ft. wide?

9. A rectangle having an area of 48 sq. in. is three times as long as wide. What are the dimensions?

10. The length of a rectangle is four times the width. If the perimeter is 60 ft., what is the area?

11. From two adjacent sides of a rectangular field 60 rd. long and 40 rd. wide a road is cut 4 rd. wide. How many acres are cut off for the road?

12. From one end of a rectangular sheet of iron 10 in. long a square piece is cut off leaving 25 sq. in. in the rest of the sheet. How wide is the sheet?

Proposition IV. Theorem

322. *The area of a parallelogram is equal to the product of its base by its altitude.*

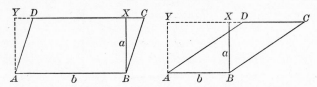

Given the parallelogram *ABCD*, with base *b* and altitude *a*.

To prove that the area of the $\square ABCD = ab$.

Proof. From *B* draw $BX \perp$ to *CD* or to *CD* produced, and from *A* draw $AY \perp$ to *CD* produced.

Then *ABXY* is a rectangle, with base *b* and altitude *a*.

Since $\qquad\qquad AY = BX$, and $AD = BC$, $\qquad\qquad$ § 125

$\qquad \therefore$ the rt. $\triangle\,ADY$ and BCX are congruent. $\qquad$ § 89

From *ABCY* take the $\triangle BCX$; the $\square ABXY$ is left.

From *ABCY* take the $\triangle ADY$; the $\square ABCD$ is left.

$\qquad\qquad \therefore \square ABXY = \square ABCD.$ $\qquad\qquad\qquad$ Ax. 2

$\qquad\qquad$ But the area of the $\square ABXY = ab.$ $\qquad\qquad$ § 320

$\qquad \therefore$ the area of the $\square ABCD = ab$, by Ax. 8. $\qquad$ Q.E.D

323. Corollary 1. *Parallelograms having equal bases and equal altitudes are equivalent.*

324. Corollary 2. *Parallelograms having equal bases are to each other as their altitudes; parallelograms having equal altitudes are to each other as their bases; any two parallelograms are to each other as the products of their bases by their altitudes.*

This was regarded as very interesting by the ancients, since an ignorant person might think it impossible that the areas of two parallelograms could remain the same although their perimeters differed without limit.

PROPOSITION V. THEOREM

325. *The area of a triangle is equal to half the product of its base by its altitude.*

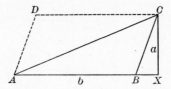

Given the triangle *ABC*, with altitude *a* and base *b*.

To prove that the area of the △ ABC = ½ ab.

Proof. With *AB* and *BC* as adjacent sides construct the parallelogram *ABCD*.   § 238

Then   △ ABC = ½ ☐ ABCD.   § 126

But   the area of the ☐ ABCD = ab.   § 322

∴ the area of the △ ABC = ½ ab, by Ax. 4.   Q. E. D.

326. COROLLARY 1. *Triangles having equal bases and equal altitudes are equivalent.*

327. COROLLARY 2. *Triangles having equal bases are to each other as their altitudes; triangles having equal altitudes are to each other as their bases; any two triangles are to each other as the products of their bases by their altitudes.*

Has this been proved for rectangles ? What is the relation of a triangle to a rectangle of equal base and equal altitude ? What must then be the relations of triangles to one another ?

328. COROLLARY 3. *The product of the sides of a right triangle is equal to the product of the hypotenuse by the altitude from the vertex of the right angle.*

How is the area of a right triangle found in terms of the sides of the right angle ? in terms of the hypotenuse and altitude ? How do these results compare ?

Proposition VI. Theorem

329. *The area of a trapezoid is equal to half the product of the sum of its bases by its altitude.*

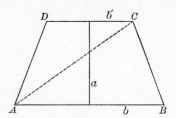

Given the trapezoid **ABCD**, with bases **b** and **b'** and altitude **a**.

To prove that the area of $ABCD = \frac{1}{2} a (b + b')$.

Proof.   Draw the diagonal AC.

Then   the area of the $\triangle ABC = \frac{1}{2} ab$,

and   the area of the $\triangle ACD = \frac{1}{2} ab'$.   § 325

∴ the area of $ABCD = \frac{1}{2} a (b + b')$, by Ax. 1.   q.e.d.

330. Corollary. *The area of a trapezoid is equal to the product of the line joining the mid-points of its nonparallel sides by its altitude.*

How is the line joining the mid-points of the nonparallel sides related to the sum of the bases (§ 137)?

331. Area of an Irregular Polygon. The area of an irregular polygon may be found by dividing the polygon into triangles, and then finding the area of each of these triangles separately.

A common method used in land surveying is as follows: Draw the longest diagonal, and let fall perpendiculars upon this diagonal from the other vertices of the polygon. The sum of the right triangles, rectangles, and trapezoids is equivalent to the polygon.

EXERCISE 51

Find the areas of the parallelograms whose bases and altitudes are respectively as follows:

1. 2.25 in., $1\frac{1}{3}$ in. **3.** 2.7 ft., 1.2 ft. **5.** 2 ft. 3 in., 7 in.

2. 3.44 in., $1\frac{1}{2}$ in. **4.** 5.6 ft., 2.3 ft. **6.** 3 ft. 6 in., 2 ft.

Find the areas of the triangles whose bases and altitudes are respectively as follows:

7. 1.4 in., $1\frac{1}{2}$ in. **9.** $6\frac{1}{2}$ ft., 3 ft. **11.** 1 ft. 6 in., 8 in.

8. 2.5 in., 0.8 in. **10.** 5.4 ft., 1.2 ft. **12.** 3 ft. 8 in., 3 ft.

Find the areas of the trapezoids whose bases are the first two of the following numbers, and whose altitudes are the third numbers:

13. 2 ft., 1 ft., 6 in. **15.** 3 ft. 7 in., 2 ft., 14 in.

14. $2\frac{1}{2}$ ft., $1\frac{1}{4}$ ft., 9 in. **16.** 5 ft. 6 in., 3 ft., 2 ft.

Find the altitudes of the parallelograms whose areas and bases are respectively as follows:

17. 10 sq. in., 5 in. **19.** 28 sq. ft., 7 ft. **21.** 30 sq. ft., 12 ft.

18. 6 sq. in., 6 in. **20.** 27 sq. ft., 6 ft. **22.** 80 sq. in., 16 in.

Find the altitudes of the triangles whose areas and bases are respectively as follows:

23. 49 sq. in., 14 in. **25.** 50 sq. ft., 10 ft. **27.** 110 sq. yd., 10 yd.

24. 48 sq. in., 12 in. **26.** 160 sq. ft., 20 ft. **28.** 176 sq. yd., 32 yd.

Find the altitudes of the trapezoids whose areas and bases are respectively as follows:

29. 33 sq. in., 5 in., 6 in. **31.** 13 sq. ft., 9 ft., 5 ft.

30. 15 sq. in., 4 in., 6 in. **32.** 70 sq. yd., 9 yd., 11 yd.

Proposition VII. Theorem

332. *The areas of two triangles that have an angle of the one equal to an angle of the other are to each other as the products of the sides including the equal angles.*

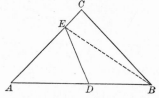

Given the triangles *ABC* and *ADE*, with the common angle *A*.

To prove that $\dfrac{\triangle ABC}{\triangle ADE} = \dfrac{AB \times AC}{AD \times AE}.$

Proof. Draw *BE*.

Then $\dfrac{\triangle ABC}{\triangle ABE} = \dfrac{AC}{AE},$

and $\dfrac{\triangle ABE}{\triangle ADE} = \dfrac{AB}{AD}.$ § 327

(Triangles having equal altitudes are to each other as their bases.)

Since we are considering numerical measures of area and length, we may treat all of the terms of these proportions as numbers.

Taking the product of the first members and the product of the second members of these equations, we have

$$\frac{\triangle ABE \times \triangle ABC}{\triangle ADE \times \triangle ABE} = \frac{AB \times AC}{AD \times AE}.$$ Ax. 3

That is, by canceling $\triangle ABE$, we have the proportion

$$\frac{\triangle ABC}{\triangle ADE} = \frac{AB \times AC}{AD \times AE}.$$ Q. E. D.

Proposition VIII. Theorem

333. *The areas of two similar triangles are to each other as the squares on any two corresponding sides.*

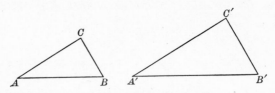

Given the similar triangles *ABC* and *A'B'C'*.

To prove that $\dfrac{\triangle ABC}{\triangle A'B'C'} = \dfrac{\overline{AB}^2}{\overline{A'B'}^2}$.

Proof. Since the triangles are similar,   Given

$$\therefore \angle A = \angle A'. \qquad\qquad \text{§ 282}$$

Then $\dfrac{\triangle ABC}{\triangle A'B'C'} = \dfrac{AB \times AC}{A'B' \times A'C'}$.   § 332

(The areas of two triangles that have an angle of the one equal to an angle of the other are to each other as the products of the sides including the equal angles.)

That is, $\dfrac{\triangle ABC}{\triangle A'B'C'} = \dfrac{AB}{A'B'} \times \dfrac{AC}{A'C'}$.

But $\dfrac{AB}{A'B'} = \dfrac{AC}{A'C'}$.   § 282

(Similar polygons have their corresponding sides proportional.)

Substituting $\dfrac{AB}{A'B'}$ for its equal $\dfrac{AC}{A'C'}$, we have

$$\dfrac{\triangle ABC}{\triangle A'B'C'} = \dfrac{AB}{A'B'} \times \dfrac{AB}{A'B'}, \qquad \text{Ax. 9}$$

or $\dfrac{\triangle ABC}{\triangle A'B'C'} = \dfrac{\overline{AB}^2}{\overline{A'B'}^2}$.   Q.E.D.

Proposition IX. Theorem

334. *The areas of two similar polygons are to each other as the squares on any two corresponding sides.*

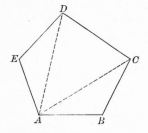 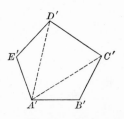

Given the similar polygons *ABCDE* and *A'B'C'D'E'*, of area *s* and *s'* respectively.

To prove that $s : s' = \overline{AB}^2 : \overline{A'B'}^2$.

Proof. By drawing all the diagonals from any corresponding vertices *A* and *A'*, the two similar polygons are divided into similar triangles.   § 292

$$\therefore \frac{\triangle ADE}{\triangle A'D'E'} = \frac{\overline{AD}^2}{\overline{A'D'}^2} = \frac{\triangle ACD}{\triangle A'C'D'} = \frac{\overline{AC}^2}{\overline{A'C'}^2} = \frac{\triangle ABC}{\triangle A'B'C'} = \frac{\overline{AB}^2}{\overline{A'B'}^2}. \quad \text{§ 333}$$

That is, $\dfrac{\triangle ADE}{\triangle A'D'E'} = \dfrac{\triangle ACD}{\triangle A'C'D'} = \dfrac{\triangle ABC}{\triangle A'B'C'}.$ Ax. 8

$$\therefore \frac{\triangle ADE + \triangle ACD + \triangle ABC}{\triangle A'D'E' + \triangle A'C'D' + \triangle A'B'C'} = \frac{\triangle ABC}{\triangle A'B'C'} = \frac{\overline{AB}^2}{\overline{A'B'}^2} \quad \text{§ 269}$$

$$\therefore s : s' = \overline{AB}^2 : \overline{A'B'}^2, \text{ by Ax. 11.} \qquad \text{Q.E.D.}$$

335. Corollary 1. *The areas of two similar polygons are to each other as the squares on any two corresponding lines.*

336. Corollary 2. *Corresponding sides of two similar polygons have the same ratio as the square roots of the areas.*

Proposition X. Theorem

337. *The square on the hypotenuse of a right triangle is equivalent to the sum of the squares on the other two sides.*

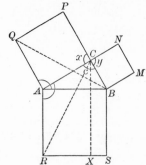

Given the right triangle *ABC*, with *AS* the square on the hypotenuse, and *BN*, *CQ* the squares on the other two sides.

To prove that $AS = BN + CQ.$

Proof.   Draw *CX* through *C* ∥ to *BS*.   § 233

Draw *CR* and *BQ*.

Since ∠ *c* and *x* are rt. ∠, the ∠ *PCB* is a straight angle, § 34

and the line *PCB* is a straight line.   § 43

Similarly, the line *ACN* is a straight line.

In the △ *ARC* and *ABQ*,

$$AR = AB,$$

$$AC = AQ,$$ § 65

and   ∠ *RAC* = ∠ *BAQ*.   Ax. 1

(Each is the sum of a rt. ∠ and the ∠ BAC.)

∴ △ *ARC* is congruent to △ *ABQ*.   § 68

Furthermore the □ *AX* is double the △ *ARC*.   § 325

(They have the same base AR, and the same altitude RX.)

Again the square CQ is double the $\triangle ABQ$.   § 325

(They have the same base AQ, and the same altitude AC.)

∴. the $\square\, AX$ is equivalent to the square CQ.   Ax. 3

In like manner, by drawing CS and AM, it may be proved that the rectangle BX is equivalent to the square BN.

Since   square $AS = \square\, BX + \square\, AX$,   Ax. 11

∴ $AS = BN + CQ$, by Ax. 9.   Q.E.D.

The first proof of this theorem is usually attributed to Pythagoras (about 525 B.C.), although the truth of the proposition was known earlier. It is one of the most important propositions of geometry. Various proofs may be given, but the one here used is the most common. This proof is attributed to Euclid (about 300 B.C.), a famous Greek geometer.

338. COROLLARY 1. *The square on either side of a right triangle is equivalent to the difference of the square on the hypotenuse and the square on the other side.*

339. COROLLARY 2. *The diagonal and a side of a square are incommensurable.*

For $\overline{AC}^2 = \overline{AB}^2 + \overline{BC}^2 = 2\,\overline{AB}^2.$

∴ $AC = AB\sqrt{2}.$

Since $\sqrt{2}$ may be carried to as many decimal places as we please, but cannot be exactly expressed as a rational fraction, it has no common measure with 1. That is, $AC : AB = \sqrt{2}$, an incommensurable number.

340. Projection. If from the extremities of a line-segment perpendiculars are let fall upon another line, the segment thus cut off is called the *projection* of the first line upon the second.

Thus $C'D'$ is the projection of CD upon AB, or l' is the projection of l upon AB.

In general it is convenient to designate by the small letter a the side of a triangle opposite $\angle A$, and so for the other sides; to designate the projection of a by a'; and to designate the height (altitude) by h.

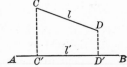

EXERCISE 52

Given the sides of a right triangle as follows, find the hypotenuse to two decimal places:

  1. 30 ft., 40 ft.   **3.** 20 ft., 30 ft.   **5.** 2 ft. 6 in., 3 ft.

  2. 45 ft., 60 ft.   **4.** 1.5 in., 2.5 in.   **6.** 3 ft. 8 in., 2 ft.

Given the hypotenuse and one side of a right triangle as follows, find the other side to two decimal places:

  7. 50 ft., 40 ft.   **9.** 10 ft., 6 ft.   **11.** 3 ft. 4 in., 2 ft.

  8. 35 ft., 21 ft.   **10.** 1.2 in., 0.8 in.   **12.** 6 ft. 2 in., 5 ft.

13. A ladder 38 ft. 6 in. long is placed against a wall, with its foot 23.1 ft. from the base of the wall. How high does it reach on the wall ?

14. Find the altitude of an equilateral triangle with side s.

15. Find the side of an equilateral triangle with altitude h.

16. The area of an equilateral triangle with side s is $\frac{1}{4} s^2 \sqrt{3}$.

17. Find the length of the longest chord and of the shortest chord that can be drawn through a point 1 ft. from the center of a circle whose radius is 20 in.

18. The radius of a circle is 5 in. Through a point 3 in. from the center a diameter is drawn, and also a chord perpendicular to the diameter. Find the length of this chord, and the distance (to two decimal places) from one end of the chord to the ends of the diameter.

19. In this figure the angle C is a right angle. From the relations $\overline{AC}^2 = AB \times AF$ (§ 294) and $\overline{CB}^2 = AB \times BF$, show that $\overline{AC}^2 + \overline{CB}^2 = \overline{AB}^2$.

20. If the diagonals of a quadrilateral intersect at right angles, the sum of the squares on one pair of opposite sides is equivalent to the sum of the squares on the other pair.

Proposition XI. Theorem

341. *In any triangle the square on the side opposite an acute angle is equivalent to the sum of the squares on the other two sides diminished by twice the product of one of those sides by the projection of the other upon that side.*

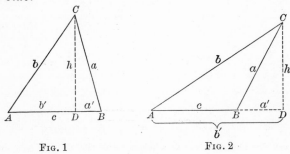

Fig. 1   Fig. 2

Given the triangle ABC, A being an acute angle, and a' and b' being the projections of a and b respectively upon c.

To prove that $a^2 = b^2 + c^2 - 2\,b'c.$

Proof. If D, the foot of the $\perp$ from C, falls upon c (Fig. 1),
$$a' = c - b'.$$

If D falls upon c produced (Fig. 2),
$$a' = b' - c.$$

In either case, by squaring, we have
$$a'^2 = b'^2 + c^2 - 2\,b'c. \qquad \text{Ax. 5}$$

Adding h^2 to each side of this equation, we have
$$h^2 + a'^2 = h^2 + b'^2 + c^2 - 2\,b'c. \qquad \text{Ax. 1}$$

But $h^2 + a'^2 = a^2$, and $h^2 + b'^2 = b^2.$ § 337

Putting a^2 and b^2 for their equals in the above equation, we have $a^2 = b^2 + c^2 - 2\,b'c$, by Ax. 9.   Q. E. D.

Proposition XII. Theorem

342. *In any obtuse triangle the square on the side opposite the obtuse angle is equivalent to the sum of the squares on the other two sides increased by twice the product of one of those sides by the projection of the other upon that side.*

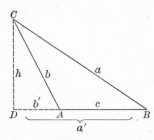

Given the obtuse triangle ABC, A being the obtuse angle, and a' and b' the projections of a and b respectively upon c.

To prove that $\qquad a^2 = b^2 + c^2 + 2\,b'c.$

Proof. $\qquad\qquad a' = b' + c.$ $\hfill$ Ax. 11

Squaring, $\qquad\quad a'^2 = b'^2 + c^2 + 2\,b'c.$ $\hfill$ Ax. 5

Adding h^2 to each side of this equation, we have

$$h^2 + a'^2 = h^2 + b'^2 + c^2 + 2\,b'c. \qquad \text{Ax. 1}$$

But $\qquad h^2 + a'^2 = a^2$, and $h^2 + b'^2 = b^2.$ $\hfill$ § 337

Putting a^2 and b^2 for their equals in the above equation, we have

$$a^2 = b^2 + c^2 + 2\,b'c, \text{ by Ax. 9.} \qquad \text{Q. E. D.}$$

Discussion. By the Principle of Continuity the last three theorems may be included in one theorem by letting the $\angle A$ change from an acute angle to a right angle and then to an obtuse angle. Let the student explain.

The last three theorems enable us to compute the altitudes of a triangle if the three sides are known; for in Prop. XII we can find b', and from b and b' we can find h.

EXERCISE 53

Find the lengths, to two decimal places, of the diagonals of the squares whose sides are:

1. 7 in.   **2.** 10 in.   **3.** 9.2 in.   **4.** 1 ft. 6 in.   **5.** 2 ft. 3 in.

Find the lengths, to two decimal places, of the sides of the squares whose diagonals are:

6. 4 in.   **7.** 8 in.   **8.** 5 ft.   **9.** $\sqrt{5}$ in.   **10.** 2 ft. 6 in.

11. The minute hand and hour hand of a clock are 6 in. and $4\frac{1}{2}$ in. long respectively. How far apart are the ends of the hands at 9 o'clock?

12. A rectangle whose base is 9 and diagonal 15 has the same area as a square whose side is x. Find the value of x.

13. A ring is screwed into a ceiling in a room 10 ft. high. Two rings are screwed into the floor at points 5 ft. and 12 ft. from a point directly beneath the one in the ceiling. Wires are stretched from the ceiling ring to each floor ring. How long are the wires? (Answer to two decimal places.)

14. The sum of the squares on the segments of two perpendicular chords is equivalent to the square on the diameter of the circle.

If AB, CD are the chords, draw the diameter BE, and draw AC, ED, BD. Prove that $AC = ED$.

15. The difference of the squares on two sides of a triangle is equivalent to the difference of the squares on the segments of the third side, made by the perpendicular on the third side from the opposite vertex.

16. In an isosceles triangle the square on one of the equal sides is equivalent to the square on any line drawn from the vertex to the base, increased by the product of the segments of the base.

Proposition XIII. Theorem

343. *The sum of the squares on two sides of a triangle is equivalent to twice the square on half the third side, increased by twice the square on the median upon that side.*

The difference of the squares on two sides of a triangle is equivalent to twice the product of the third side by the projection of the median upon that side.

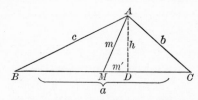

Given the triangle ABC, the median m, and m' the projection of m upon the side a. Also let c be greater than b.

To prove that   1. $c^2 + b^2 = 2\,\overline{BM}^2 + 2\,m^2$;

                    2. $c^2 - b^2 = 2\,am'$.

Proof. The $\angle AMB$ is obtuse, and the $\angle CMA$ is acute.   § 116

          Since $c > b$, M lies between B and D.   § 84

Then $c^2 = \overline{BM}^2 + m^2 + 2\,BM \cdot m'$,   § 342

and $b^2 = \overline{MC}^2 + m^2 - 2\,MC \cdot m'$.   § 341

Adding these equals, and observing that $BM = MC$, we have

$$c^2 + b^2 = 2\,\overline{BM}^2 + 2\,m^2. \qquad\qquad \text{Ax. 1}$$

Subtracting the second from the first, we have

$$c^2 - b^2 = 2\,am', \text{ by Ax. 2.} \qquad\qquad \text{Q.E.D.}$$

Discussion. Consider the proposition when $c = b$.

This theorem may be omitted without interfering with the regular sequence. It enables us to compute the medians when the three sides are known.

EXERCISE 54

1. To compute the area of a triangle in terms of its sides.

At least one of the angles A or B is acute. Suppose A is acute.

In the $\triangle ADC$, $h^2 = b^2 - \overline{AD}^2$.   Why?

In the $\triangle ABC$, $a^2 = b^2 + c^2 - 2\,c \times AD$.   Why?

Therefore $AD = \dfrac{b^2 + c^2 - a^2}{2\,c}$.

Hence $h^2 = b^2 - \dfrac{(b^2 + c^2 - a^2)^2}{4\,c^2} = \dfrac{4\,b^2c^2 - (b^2 + c^2 - a^2)^2}{4\,c^2}$

$$= \frac{(2\,bc + b^2 + c^2 - a^2)\,(2\,bc - b^2 - c^2 + a^2)}{4\,c^2}$$

$$= \frac{\{(b + c)^2 - a^2\}\,\{a^2 - (b - c)^2\}}{4\,c^2}$$

$$= \frac{(a + b + c)\,(b + c - a)\,(a + b - c)\,(a - b + c)}{4\,c^2}.$$

Let $a + b + c = 2\,s$, where s stands for semiperimeter.

Then $b + c - a = a + b + c - 2\,a = 2\,s - 2\,a = 2\,(s - a)$.

Similarly $a + b - c = 2\,(s - c)$,

and $a - b + c = 2\,(s - b)$.

Hence $h^2 = \dfrac{2\,s \times 2\,(s - a) \times 2\,(s - b) \times 2\,(s - c)}{4\,c^2}$.

By simplifying, and extracting the square root,

$$h = \frac{2}{c}\sqrt{s\,(s - a)\,(s - b)\,(s - c)}.$$

Hence the area $= \tfrac{1}{2}\,ch = \sqrt{s\,(s - a)\,(s - b)\,(s - c)}$.

For example, if the sides are 3, 4, and 5,

$$\text{area} = \sqrt{6\,(6 - 3)\,(6 - 4)\,(6 - 5)} = \sqrt{6 \cdot 3 \cdot 2} = 6.$$

If Ex. 1 has been studied, find the areas, to two decimal places, of the triangles whose sides are:

2. 4, 5, 6.   **4.** 6, 8, 10.   **6.** 7, 8, 11.   **8.** 1.2, 3, 2.1.

3. 5, 6, 7.   **5.** 6, 8, 9.   **7.** 9, 10, 11.   **9.** 11, 12, 13.

10. To compute the radius of the circle circumscribed about a triangle in terms of the sides of the triangle. (Solve only if § 305 and Ex. 1 have been taken.)

Let CD be a diameter.

By § 305, what do we know about the products $CA \times BC$ and $CD \times CP$? What does this tell us of ab and $2 r \cdot CP$, r being the radius?

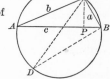

From Ex. 1, what does CP equal in terms of the sides?

Is it therefore possible to show that

$$r = \frac{abc}{4\sqrt{s(s-a)(s-b)(s-c)}}\ ?$$

If Exs. 1 and 10 have been studied, compute the radii, to two decimal places, of the circles circumscribed about the triangles whose sides are:

11. 3, 4, 5.   **12.** 27, 36, 45.   **13.** 7, 9, 11.   **14.** 10, 11, 12.

15. To compute the medians of a triangle in terms of its sides.

Omit if § 343 has not been taken. What do we know about $a^2 + b^2$ as compared with $2\,m^2 + 2\left(\dfrac{c}{2}\right)^2$?

From this relation show that

$$m = \tfrac{1}{2}\sqrt{2(a^2 + b^2) - c^2}.$$

If Ex. 15 has been studied, compute the three medians, to two decimal places, of the triangles whose sides are:

16. 3, 4, 5.   **17.** 6, 8, 10.   **18.** 6, 7, 8.   **19.** 7, 9, 11.

20. If the sides of a triangle are 7, 9, and 11, is the angle opposite the side 11 right, acute, or obtuse?

21. The square constructed upon the sum of two lines is equivalent to the sum of the squares constructed upon these two lines, increased by twice the rectangle of these lines.

Given the two lines AB and BC, and AC their sum. Construct the squares $AKGC$ and $ADEB$ upon AC and AB respectively. Produce BE and DE to meet KG and CG in H and F respectively. Then we have the square $EHGF$, with sides each equal to BC. Hence the square $AKGC$ is the sum of the squares $ADEB$ and $EHGF$, and the rectangles $DKHE$ and $BEFC$.

This proves geometrically the algebraic formula
$$(a + b)^2 = a^2 + 2\,ab + b^2.$$

22. The square constructed upon the difference of two lines is equivalent to the sum of the squares constructed upon these two lines, diminished by twice their rectangle.

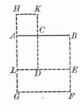

Given the two lines AB and AC, and BC their difference. Construct the square $AGFB$ upon AB, the square $ACKH$ upon AC, and the square $CDEB$ upon BC. Produce ED to meet AG in L. The dimensions of the rectangles $LGFE$ and $HLDK$ are AB and AC, and the square $CDEB$ is the difference between the whole figure and the sum of these rectangles.

This proves geometrically the algebraic formula
$$(a - b)^2 = a^2 - 2\,ab + b^2.$$

23. The difference between the squares constructed upon two lines is equivalent to the rectangle of the sum and difference of these lines.

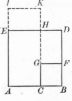

Given the squares $ABDE$ and $CBFG$, constructed upon AB and BC. The difference between these squares is the polygon $ACGFDE$, which is composed of the rectangles $ACHE$ and $GFDH$. Produce AE and CH to I and K respectively, making EI and HK each equal to BC, and draw IK. The difference between the squares $ABDE$ and $CBFG$ is then equivalent to the rectangle $ACKI$, with dimensions $AB + BC$, and $AB - BC$.

This proves geometrically the algebraic formula
$$a^2 - b^2 = (a + b)\,(a - b).$$

PROPOSITION XIV. PROBLEM

344. *To construct a square equivalent to the sum of two given squares.*

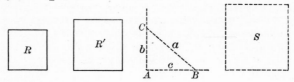

Given the two squares, R and R'.

Required to construct a square equivalent to $R + R'$.

Construction. Construct the rt. $\angle A$. § 228

On the sides of $\angle A$, take AB, or c, equal to a side of R', and AC, or b, equal to a side of R, and draw BC, or a.

Construct the square S, having a side equal to BC.

Then S is the square required. Q.E.F.

Proof. $$a^2 = b^2 + c^2.$$ § 337

(*The square on the hypotenuse of a rt. $\triangle$ is equivalent to the sum of the squares on the other two sides.*)

$$\therefore \ S = R + R', \text{ by Ax. 9.} \qquad \text{Q.E.D.}$$

345. COROLLARY 1. *To construct a square equivalent to the difference of two given squares.*

We may easily reverse the above construction by first drawing c, then erecting a $\perp$ at A, and then with a radius a fixing the point C.

346. COROLLARY 2. *To construct a square equivalent to the sum of three given squares.*

If a side of the third square is d, we may erect a perpendicular from C to the line BC, take CD equal to d, and join D and B.

Discussion. It is evident that we can continue this process indefinitely, and thus construct a square equivalent to the sum of any number of given squares.

Proposition XV. Problem

347. *To construct a polygon similar to two given similar polygons and equivalent to their sum.*

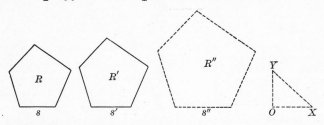

Given the two similar polygons R and R'.

Required to construct a polygon similar to R and R', and equivalent to $R + R'$.

Construction.   Construct the rt. $\angle O$.   § 228

  Let s and s' be corresponding sides of R and R'.

On the sides of $\angle O$, take OX equal to s', and OY equal to s.

  Draw XY, and take s'' equal to XY.

Upon s'', corresponding to s, construct R'' similar to R.   § 312

  Then R'' is the polygon required.   Q.E.F.

Proof. $\overline{OY}^2 + \overline{OX}^2 = \overline{XY}^2.$ § 337

Putting for OY, OX, and XY their equals s, s', and s'', we have

$$s^2 + s'^2 = s''^2.$$ Ax. 9

But $$\frac{R}{R''} = \frac{s^2}{s''^2},$$

and $$\frac{R'}{R''} = \frac{s'^2}{s''^2}.$$ § 334

By addition, $$\frac{R + R'}{R''} = \frac{s^2 + s'^2}{s''^2} = 1.$$ Ax. 1

$$\therefore R'' = R + R', \text{ by Ax. 3.}$$ Q.E.D.

Proposition XVI. Problem

348. *To construct a triangle equivalent to a given
polygon.*

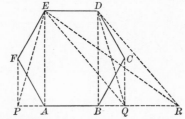

Given the polygon *ABCDEF*.

Required to construct a triangle equivalent to ABCDEF.

Construction. Let *B*, *C*, and *D* be any three consecutive
vertices of the polygon. Draw the diagonal *DB*.

From C draw a line ‖ to DB.   § 233

Produce *AB* to meet this line at *Q*, and draw *DQ*.

Again, draw *EQ*, and from *D* draw a line ‖ to *EQ*, meeting
AB produced at *R*, and draw *ER*.

In like manner continue to reduce the number of sides of
the polygon until we obtain the △ *EPR*.

Then △ *EPR* is the triangle required.   Q. E. F.

Proof. The polygon *AQDEF* has one side less than the
polygon *ABCDEF*.

Furthermore, in the two polygons, the part *ABDEF* is common,

and the △ *BQD* = △ *BCD*.   § 326

(*For the base DB is common, and their vertices C and Q are in
the line CQ ‖ to the base.*)

∴ *AQDEF* = *ABCDEF*.   Ax. 1

In like manner it may be proved that

AREF = *AQDEF*, and *EPR* = *AREF*.   Q. E. D.

Proposition XVII. Problem

349. *To construct a square equivalent to a given parallelogram.*

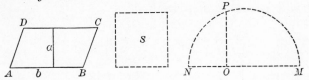

Given the parallelogram *ABCD*.

Required to construct a square equivalent to the □ABCD.

Construction. Upon any convenient line take *NO* equal to *a*, and *OM* equal to *b*, the altitude and base respectively of □ *ABCD*.

Upon *NM* as a diameter describe a semicircle.

At *O* erect *OP* ⊥ to *NM*, meeting the circle at *P*.   § 228

Construct the square *S*, having a side equal to *OP*.

Then *S* is the square required.   Q.E.F.

Proof. $NO : OP = OP : OM.$ § 297

$$\therefore \overline{OP}^2 = NO \times OM.$$ § 261

That is, $\overline{OP}^2 = ab.$ Ax. 9

But $S = \overline{OP}^2,$

and $\square ABCD = ab.$ § 322

$\therefore S = \square ABCD,$ by Ax. 9.   Q.E.D.

350. Corollary 1. *To construct a square equivalent to a given triangle.*

Take for a side of the square the mean proportional between the base and half the altitude of the triangle.

351. Corollary 2. *To construct a square equivalent to a given polygon*

First reduce the polygon to an equivalent triangle, and then construct a square equivalent to the triangle.

Proposition XVIII. Problem

352. *To construct a parallelogram equivalent to a given square, and having the sum of its base and altitude equal to a given line.*

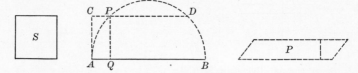

Given the square *S*, and the line *AB*.

Required to construct a ▱ equivalent to S, with the sum of its base and altitude equal to AB.

Construction. Upon *AB* as a diameter describe a semicircle.

At *A* erect *AC* ⊥ to *AB* and equal to a side of the given square *S*.   § 228

Draw *CD* ∥ to *AB*, cutting the circle at *P*.   § 233

Draw *PQ* ⊥ to *AB*.   § 227

Then any ▱, as *P*, having *AQ* for its altitude and *QB* for its base is equivalent to *S*.   Q.E.F.

Proof. $AQ : PQ = PQ : QB.$ § 297

$$\therefore \overline{PQ}^2 = AQ \times QB. \qquad \text{§ 261}$$

Furthermore PQ is ∥ to CA.   § 95

$$\therefore PQ = CA. \qquad \text{§ 127}$$

$$\therefore \overline{PQ}^2 = \overline{CA}^2. \qquad \text{Ax. 5}$$

$$\therefore AQ \times QB = \overline{CA}^2. \qquad \text{Ax. 8}$$

But $P = AQ \times QB,$ § 322

and $S = \overline{CA}^2.$ § 320

$$\therefore P = S, \text{ by Ax. 8.} \qquad \text{Q.E.D.}$$

Thus is solved geometrically the algebraic problem, given $x + y = a$, $xy = b$, to find x and y.

Proposition XIX. Problem

353. *To construct a parallelogram equivalent to a given square, and having the difference of its base and altitude equal to a given line.*

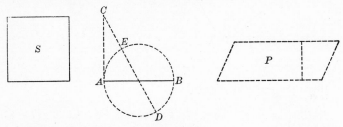

Given the square *S*, and the line *AB*.

Required to construct a $\square$ equivalent to S, with the difference of its base and altitude equal to AB.

Construction. Upon AB as a diameter describe a circle.

From A draw AC, tangent to the circle,   § 246

and equal to a side of the given square S.

Through the center of the circle draw CD intersecting the circle at E and D.

Then any $\square$, as P, having CD for its base and CE for its altitude, is equivalent to S.   Q. E. F.

Proof. $CD : CA = CA : CE.$ § 302

$$\therefore \overline{CA}^2 = CD \times CE,$$ § 261

and the difference between CD and CE is the diameter of the circle, that is, AB.

But $P = CD \times CE,$ § 322

and $S = \overline{CA}^2.$ § 320

$$\therefore P = S, \text{ by Ax. 8.}$$ Q. E. D.

Thus is solved geometrically the algebraic problem, given $x - y = a$, $xy = b$, to find x and y.

Proposition XX. Problem

354. *To construct a polygon similar to a given polygon and equivalent to another given polygon.*

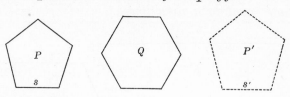

Given the polygons *P* and *Q*.

Required to construct a polygon similar to P and equivalent to Q.

Construction. Construct squares equivalent to *P* and *Q*, § 351
and let *m* and *n* respectively denote their sides.

Let *s* be any side of *P*.

Find *s'*, the fourth proportional to *m*, *n*, and *s*.   § 307

Upon *s'*, corresponding to *s*,

construct a polygon *P'* similar to the polygon *P*.   § 312

Then   *P'* is the polygon required.   Q.E.F.

Proof. Since $m : n = s : s'$,   Const.

$$\therefore m^2 : n^2 = s^2 : s'^2.$$ § 270

But $P = m^2$, and $Q = n^2$.   Const.

$$\therefore P : Q = s^2 : s'^2.$$ Ax. 9

But $P : P' = s^2 : s'^2$.   § 334

(*The areas of two similar polygons are to each other as the squares on any two corresponding sides.*)

$$\therefore P : Q = P : P'.$$ Ax. 8

$$\therefore P' = Q.$$ § 263

$\therefore$ *P'*, being similar to *P*, is the polygon required. Q.E.D.

Proposition XXI. Problem

355. *To construct a square which shall have a given ratio to a given square.*

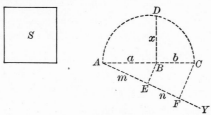

Given the square S, and the ratio $\dfrac{n}{m}$.

Required to construct a square which shall be to S as n is to m.

Construction. Take AB equal to a side of S, and draw AY, making any convenient angle with AB.

On AY take AE equal to m units and EF equal to n units.

Draw EB.

From F draw a line ∥ to EB, meeting AB produced at C.   § 233

On AC as a diameter describe a semicircle.

At B erect $BD \perp$ to AC, meeting the semicircle at D.   § 228

Then BD is a side of the square required.   Q.E.F.

Proof. Denote AB by a, BC by b, and BD by x.

Then $a : x = x : b$.   § 297

$\therefore a : b = a^2 : x^2$.   § 271

But $a : b = m : n$.   § 273

$\therefore a^2 : x^2 = m : n$.   Ax. 8

By inversion, $x^2 : a^2 = n : m$.   § 266

Hence the square on BD will have the same ratio to S as n has to m.   Q.E.D.

Proposition XXII. Problem

356. *To construct a polygon similar to a given polygon and having a given ratio to it.*

Given the polygon P and the ratio $\dfrac{n}{m}$.

Required to construct a polygon similar to P, which shall be to P as n is to m.

Construction. Let s be any side of P.

Draw a line s', such that the square on s' shall be to the square on s as n is to m. § 355

Upon s' as a side corresponding to s construct the polygon P' similar to P. § 312

(*Upon a given line corresponding to a given side of a given polygon, to construct a polygon similar to the given polygon.*)

Then P' is the polygon required. Q. E. F.

Proof. $P' : P = s'^2 : s^2$. § 334

(*The areas of two similar polygons are to each other as the squares on any two corresponding sides.*)

But $s'^2 : s^2 = n : m$. Const.

Therefore $P' : P = n : m$, by Ax. 8. Q. E. D.

This problem enables us to construct a square that is twice a given square or half a given square, to construct an equilateral triangle that shall be any number of times a given equilateral triangle, and in general to enlarge or to reduce any figure in a given ratio. An architect's drawing, for example, might need to be enlarged so as to be double the area of the original, and the scale could be found by this method.

EXERCISE 55

Problems of Computation

1. The sides of a triangle are 0.7 in., 0.6 in., and 0.7 in. respectively. Is the largest angle acute, right, or obtuse?

2. The sides of a triangle are 5.1 in., 6.8 in., and 8.5 in. respectively. Is the largest angle acute, right, or obtuse?

3. Find the area of an isosceles triangle whose perimeter is 14 in. and base 4 in. (One decimal place.)

4. Find the area of an equilateral triangle whose perimeter is 18 in. (One decimal place.)

5. Find the area of a right triangle, the hypotenuse being 1.7 in. and one of the other sides being 0.8 in.

6. Find the ratio of the altitudes of two triangles of equal area, the base of one being 1.5 in. and that of the other 4.5 in.

7. The bases of a trapezoid are 34 in. and 30 in., and the altitude is 2 in. Find the side of a square having the same area.

8. What is the area of the isosceles right triangle in which the hypotenuse is $\sqrt{2}$?

9. What is the area of the isosceles right triangle in which the hypotenuse is $7\sqrt{2}$?

10. If the side of an equilateral triangle is $2\sqrt{3}$, what is the altitude of the triangle? the area of the triangle?

11. If the side of an equilateral triangle is 1 ft., what is the area of the triangle?

12. If the area of an equilateral triangle is 43.3 sq. in., what is the base of the triangle? (Take $\sqrt{3} = 1.732$.)

13. The sides of a triangle are 2.8 in., 3.5 in., and 2.1 in. respectively. Draw the figure carefully and see what kind of a triangle it is. Verify this conclusion by applying a geometric test, and find the area of the triangle.

EXERCISE 56

THEOREMS

1. The area of a rhombus is equal to half the product of its diagonals.

2. Two triangles are equivalent if the base of the first is equal to half the altitude of the second, and the altitude of the first is equal to twice the base of the second.

3. The area of a circumscribed polygon is equal to half the product of its perimeter by the radius of the inscribed circle.

4. Two parallelograms are equivalent if their altitudes are reciprocally proportional to their bases.

5. If equilateral triangles are constructed on the sides of a right triangle, the triangle on the hypotenuse is equivalent to the sum of the triangles on the other two sides.

6. If similar polygons are constructed on the sides of a right triangle, as corresponding sides, the polygon on the hypotenuse is equivalent to the sum of the polygons on the other two sides.

Ex. 6 is one of the general forms of the Pythagorean Theorem.

7. If lines are drawn from any point within a parallelogram to the four vertices, the sum of either pair of triangles with parallel bases is equivalent to the sum of the other pair.

8. Every line drawn through the intersection of the diagonals of a parallelogram bisects the parallelogram.

9. The line that bisects the bases of a trapezoid divides the trapezoid into two equivalent parts.

10. If a quadrilateral with two sides parallel is bisected by either diagonal, the quadrilateral is a parallelogram.

11. The triangle formed by two lines drawn from the midpoint of either of the nonparallel sides of a trapezoid to the opposite vertices is equivalent to half the trapezoid.

EXERCISE 57

Problems of Construction

1. Given a square, to construct a square of half its area.

2. To construct a right triangle equivalent to a given oblique triangle.

3. To construct a triangle equivalent to the sum of two given triangles.

4. To construct a triangle equivalent to a given triangle, and having one side equal to a given line.

5. To construct a rectangle equivalent to a given parallelogram, and having its altitude equal to a given line.

6. To construct a right triangle equivalent to a given triangle, and having one of the sides of the right angle equal to a given line.

7. To construct a right triangle equivalent to a given triangle, and having its hypotenuse equal to a given line.

8. To divide a given triangle into two equivalent parts by a line through a given point P in the base.

9. To draw from a given point P in the base AB of a triangle ABC a line to AC produced, so that it may be bisected by BC.

10. To find a point within a given triangle such that the lines from this point to the vertices shall divide the triangle into three equivalent triangles.

11. To divide a given triangle into two equivalent parts by a line parallel to one of the sides.

12. Through a given point to draw a line so that the segments intercepted between the point and perpendiculars drawn to the line from two other given points may have a given ratio.

13. To find a point such that the perpendiculars from it to the sides of a given triangle shall be in the ratio p, q, r.

EXERCISE 58

Review Questions

1. What is meant by the area of a surface? Illustrate.

2. What is the difference between equivalent figures and congruent figures?

3. State two propositions relating to the ratio of one rectangle to another.

4. Given the base and altitude of a rectangle, how is the area found? Given the area and base, how is the altitude found?

5. How do you justify the expression, "the product of two lines"? "the quotient of an area by a line"?

6. Can a triangle with a perimeter of 10 in. have the same area as one with a perimeter of 1 in.? Is the same answer true for two squares?

7. Can a parallelogram with a perimeter of 10 in. have the same area as a rectangle with a perimeter of 1 in.? Is the same answer true for two rectangles?

8. Explain how the area of an irregular field with straight sides may be found by the use of the theorems of Book IV.

9. A triangle has two sides 5 and 6, including an angle of 70°, and another triangle has two sides 2 and $7\frac{1}{2}$, including an angle of 70°. What is the ratio of the areas of the triangles?

10. Two similar triangles have two corresponding sides 5 in. and 15 in. respectively. The larger triangle has how many times the area of the smaller?

11. Given the hypotenuse of an isosceles right triangle, how do you proceed to find the area?

12. Given three sides of a triangle, what test can you apply to determine whether or not it is a right triangle?

13. Suppose you wish to construct a square equivalent to a given polygon, how do you proceed?

BOOK V

REGULAR POLYGONS AND CIRCLES

357. Regular Polygon. A polygon that is both equiangular and equilateral is called a *regular polygon*.

Familiar examples of regular polygons are the equilateral triangle and the square.

It is proved in Prop. I (§ 362) that a circle may be circumscribed about, and a circle may be inscribed in, any regular polygon, and that these circles are concentric (§ 188).

358. Radius. The radius of the circle circumscribed about a regular polygon is called the *radius* of the polygon.

In this figure r is the radius of the polygon.

359. Apothem. The radius of the circle inscribed in a regular polygon is called the *apothem* of the polygon.

In the figure a is the apothem of the polygon. The apothem is evidently perpendicular to the side of the regular polygon (§ 185).

360. Center. The common center of the circles circumscribed about and inscribed in a regular polygon is called the *center* of the polygon.

In the figure O is the center of the polygon.

361. Angle at the Center. The angle between the radii drawn to the extremities of any side of a regular polygon is called the *angle at the center* of the polygon.

In the figure m is the angle at the center of the polygon. It is evidently subtended by the chord which is the side of the inscribed polygon.

Proposition I. Theorem

362. *A circle may be circumscribed about, and a circle may be inscribed in, any regular polygon.*

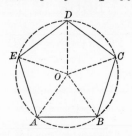

Given the regular polygon *ABCDE*.

To prove that **1.** *a circle may be circumscribed about ABCDE;*
             2. *a circle may be inscribed in ABCDE.*

Proof. 1. Let O be the center of the circle which may be passed through the three vertices A, B, and C.   § 190

Draw OA, OB, OC, OD.

Then	$OB = OC,$	§ 162
and	$AB = CD.$	§ 357
Furthermore	$\angle CBA = \angle DCB,$	§ 357
and	$\angle CBO = \angle OCB.$	§ 74
	$\therefore \angle OBA = \angle DCO.$	Ax. 2
	$\therefore \triangle OAB$ is congruent to $\triangle OCD.$	§ 68
	$\therefore OA = OD.$	§ 67

Therefore the circle that passes through A, B, C, passes also through D.

In like manner it may be proved that the circle that passes through B, C, and D passes also through E; and so on.

Therefore the circle described with O as a center and OA as a radius will be circumscribed about the polygon, by § 205.   **Q.E.D.**

Proof. 2. Let O be the center of the circumscribed circle.

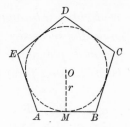

Since the sides of the regular polygon are equal chords of the circumscribed circle, they are equally distant from the center.   § 178

Therefore the circle described with O as a center, with the perpendicular from O to a side of the polygon as a radius, will be inscribed in the polygon, by § 205.   Q. E. D.

363. COROLLARY 1. *The radius drawn to any vertex of a regular polygon bisects the angle at the vertex.*

364. COROLLARY 2. *The angles at the center of any regular polygon are equal, and each is supplementary to an interior angle of the polygon.*

For the angles at the center are corresponding angles of congruent triangles. If M is the mid-point of AB, then since the $\angle MOB$ and OBM are complementary what can we say of their doubles, AOB and CBA ?

365. COROLLARY 3. *An equilateral polygon inscribed in a circle is a regular polygon.*

Why are the angles also equal ?

366. COROLLARY 4. *An equiangular polygon circumscribed about a circle is a regular polygon.*

By joining consecutive points of contact of the sides of the polygon can you show that certain isosceles triangles are congruent, and thus prove the polygon equilateral ?

Proposition II. Theorem

367. *If a circle is divided into any number of equal arcs, the chords joining the successive points of division form a regular inscribed polygon; and the tangents drawn at the points of division form a regular circumscribed polygon.*

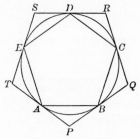

Given a circle divided into equal arcs by *A*, *B*, *C*, *D*, and *E*, *AB*, *BC*, *CD*, *DE*, and *EA* being chords, and *PQ*, *QR*, *RS*, *ST*, and *TP* being tangents at *B*, *C*, *D*, *E*, and *A* respectively.

To prove that 1. *ABCDE is a regular polygon;*

               2. *PQRST is a regular polygon.*

Proof. 1. Since the arcs are equal by construction,

$$\therefore AB = BC = CD = DE = EA. \hspace{2cm} \text{§ 170}$$

$$\therefore ABCDE \text{ is a regular polygon.} \hspace{1.5cm} \text{§ 365}$$

(*An equilateral polygon inscribed in a circle is a regular polygon.*)

Proof. 2. $\quad \angle P = \angle Q = \angle R = \angle S = \angle T. \hspace{1cm} \text{§ 221}$

(*An ∠ formed by two tangents is measured by half the difference of the intercepted arcs.*)

$$\therefore PQRST \text{ is a regular polygon.} \hspace{1.5cm} \text{§ 360}$$

(*An equiangular polygon circumscribed about a circle is a regular polygon.*)

                                     Q.E.D

368. COROLLARY 1. *Tangents to a circle at the vertices of a regular inscribed polygon form a regular circumscribed polygon of the same number of sides.*

369. COROLLARY 2. *Tangents to a circle at the mid-points of the arcs subtended by the sides of a regular inscribed polygon form a regular circumscribed polygon, whose sides are parallel to the sides of the inscribed polygon and whose vertices lie on the radii (produced) of the inscribed polygon.*

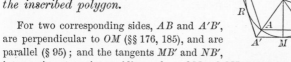

For two corresponding sides, AB and $A'B'$, are perpendicular to OM (§§ 176, 185), and are parallel (§ 95) ; and the tangents MB' and NB', intersecting at a point equidistant from OM and ON (§ 192), intersect upon the bisector of the ∠ MON (§ 152) ; that is, upon the radius OB (§ 363).

370. COROLLARY 3. *Lines drawn from each vertex of a regular polygon to the mid-points of the adjacent arcs subtended by the sides of the polygon form a regular inscribed polygon of double the number of sides.*

371. COROLLARY 4. *Tangents at the mid-points of the arcs between adjacent points of contact of the sides of a regular circumscribed polygon form a regular circumscribed polygon of double the number of sides.*

372. COROLLARY 5. *The perimeter of a regular inscribed polygon is less than that of a regular inscribed polygon of double the number of sides; and the perimeter of a regular circumscribed polygon is greater than that of a regular circumscribed polygon of double the number of sides.*

EXERCISE 59

1. Find the radius of the square whose side is 5 in.

2. Find the side of the square whose radius is 7 in.

3. Find the radius of the equilateral triangle whose side is 2 in.

4. Find the side of the equilateral triangle whose radius is 3 in.

5. Find the apothem of the equilateral triangle whose side is $\sqrt{3}$ in.

6. Find the side of the equilateral triangle whose apothem is $2\sqrt{3}$ in.

7. How many degrees are there in the angle at the center of an equiangular triangle? of a regular hexagon?

8. Given an equilateral triangle inscribed in a circle, to circumscribe an equilateral triangle about the circle.

9. Given an equilateral triangle inscribed in a circle, to inscribe a regular hexagon in the circle, and to circumscribe a regular hexagon about the circle.

10. Given a square inscribed in a circle, to inscribe a regular octagon in the circle, and to circumscribe a regular octagon about the circle.

11. How many degrees are there in the angle at the center of a regular octagon? in each angle of a regular octagon? in the sum of these two angles?

12. What is the area of the square inscribed in a circle of radius 2 in.?

13. The apothem of an equilateral triangle is equal to half the radius.

14. Prove that the apothem of an equilateral triangle is equal to one fourth the diameter of the circumscribed circle. From this show how an equilateral triangle may be inscribed in a circle.

Proposition III. Theorem

373. *Two regular polygons of the same number of sides are similar.*

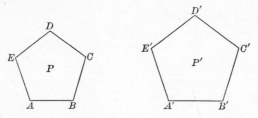

Given the regular polygons P and P', each having n sides.

To prove that P *and* P' *are similar.*

Proof. Each angle of either polygon $= \dfrac{2(n-2)}{n}$ rt. $\angle$s.   § 145

(*Each* $\angle$ *of a regular polygon of* n *sides is equal to* $\dfrac{2(n-2)}{n}$ *rt.* $\angle$s.)

Hence the polygons P and P' are mutually equiangular.

Furthermore, $\because AB = BC = CD = DE = EA$,

and $A'B' = B'C' = C'D' = D'E' = E'A'$,   § 357

$$\therefore \frac{AB}{A'B'} = \frac{BC}{B'C'} = \frac{CD}{C'D'} = \frac{DE}{D'E'} = \frac{EA}{E'A'}. \qquad \text{Ax. 4}$$

Hence the polygons have their corresponding sides proportional and their corresponding angles equal.

Therefore the two polygons are similar, by § 282. Q.E.D.

374. Corollary. *The areas of two regular polygons of the same number of sides are to each other as the squares on any two corresponding sides.*

For the areas of two similar polygons are to each other as the squares on any two corresponding sides (§ 334), and two regular polygons of the same number of sides are similar.

Proposition IV. Theorem

375. *The perimeters of two regular polygons of the same number of sides are to each other as their radii, and also as their apothems.*

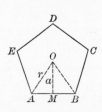 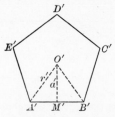

Given the regular polygons with perimeters p and p', radii r and r', apothems a and a', and centers O and O' respectively.

To prove that $\qquad p : p' = r : r' = a : a'.$

Proof. Since the polygons are similar, $\qquad$ § 373

$$\therefore p : p' = AB : A'B'. \qquad \text{§ 291}$$

Furthermore in the isosceles $\triangle OAB$ and $O'A'B'$,

$$\angle O = \angle O', \qquad \text{§ 364}$$

and $\qquad OA : OB = O'A' : O'B'. \qquad$ Ax. 8

(For each of these ratios equals 1.)

$$\therefore \text{ the } \triangle OAB \text{ and } O'A'B' \text{ are similar.} \qquad \text{§ 288}$$

$$\therefore AB : A'B' = r : r'. \qquad \text{§ 282}$$

Also $\qquad \triangle AMO$ and $A'M'O'$ are similar. $\qquad$ § 286

$$\therefore r : r' = a : a'. \qquad \text{§ 282}$$

$$\therefore p : p' = r : r' = a : a', \text{ by Ax. 8.} \qquad \text{Q. E. D.}$$

376. Corollary. *The areas of two regular polygons of the same number of sides are to each other as the squares on the radii of the circumscribed circles, and also as the squares on the radii of the inscribed circles.*

EXERCISE 60

1. Find the ratio of the perimeters and the ratio of the areas of two regular hexagons, their sides being 2 in. and 4 in. respectively.

2. Find the ratio of the perimeters and the ratio of the areas of two regular octagons, their sides having the ratio 2 : 6.

3. Find the ratio of the perimeters of two squares whose areas are 121 sq. in. and $30\frac{1}{4}$ sq. in. respectively.

4. Find the ratio of the perimeters and the ratio of the areas of two equilateral triangles whose altitudes are 3 in. and 12 in. respectively.

5. The area of one equiangular triangle is nine times that of another. Required the ratio of their altitudes.

6. The area of the cross section of a steel beam 1 in. thick is 12 sq. in. What is the area of the cross section of a beam of the same proportions and $1\frac{1}{8}$ in. thick ?

7. Squares are inscribed in two circles of radii 2 in. and 6 in. respectively. Find the ratio of the areas of the squares, and also the ratio of the perimeters.

8. Squares are inscribed in two circles of radii 2 in. and 8 in. respectively, and on the sides of these squares equilateral triangles are constructed. What is the ratio of the areas of these triangles ?

9. A round log a foot in diameter is sawed so as to have the cross section the largest square possible. What is the area of this square ? What would be the area of the cross section of the square beam cut from a log of half this diameter ?

10. Every equiangular polygon inscribed in a circle is regular if it has an odd number of sides.

11. Every equilateral polygon circumscribed about a circle is regular if it has an odd number of sides.

Proposition V. Theorem

377. *If the number of sides of a regular inscribed polygon is indefinitely increased, the apothem of the polygon approaches the radius of the circle as its limit.*

Given a regular polygon of *n* sides inscribed in the circle of radius *OA*, *s* being one side and *a* the apothem.

To prove that a approaches r as a limit, if n is increased indefinitely.

Proof. We know that $a < r$.   § 86

Then since $r - a < AM$,   § 112

and $AM < s$,   § 174

            $\therefore r - a < s$.   Ax. 10

If *n* is taken sufficiently great, *s*, and consequently $r - a$, can be made less than any assigned positive value, however small.

Since $r - a$ can become and remain less than any assigned positive value by increasing *n*, it follows that

       r is the limit of *a*, by § 204.   Q.E.D.

378. COROLLARY. *If the number of sides of a regular inscribed polygon is indefinitely increased, the square on the apothem approaches the square on the radius of the circle as its limit.*

For $r^2 - a^2 = \overline{AM}^2$.   § 338

Therefore by taking *n* sufficiently great, *s*, and consequently AM, and consequently $r^2 - a^2$, approaches zero as its limit.

Proposition VI. Theorem

379. *An arc of a circle is less than a line of any kind that envelops it on the convex side and has the same extremities.*

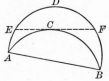

Given *BCA* an arc of a circle, *AB* being its chord.

To prove that the arc BCA is less than a line of any kind that envelops this arc and terminates at A and B.

Proof. Of all the lines that can be drawn, each to include the area *ABC* between itself and the chord *AB*, there must be at least one shortest line; for all the lines are not equal.

Let *BDA* be any kind of line enveloping *BCA* as stated.

The enveloping line *BDA* cannot be the shortest; for drawing *ECF* tangent to the arc *BCA* at any point *C*, the line *BFCEA* < *BFDEA*, since *FCE* < *FDE*.   Post. 3

In like manner it can be shown that no other enveloping line can be the shortest.

∴ *BCA* is shorter than any enveloping line.   Q.E.D.

380. Corollary. *A circle is less than the perimeter of any polygon circumscribed about it.*

381. Circle as a Limit. From Prop. VI we may now assume:

1. *The circle is the limit which the perimeters of regular inscribed polygons and of similar circumscribed polygons approach, if the number of sides of the polygons is indefinitely increased.*

2. *The area of the circle is the limit which the areas of the inscribed and circumscribed polygons approach.*

PROPOSITION VII. THEOREM

382. *Two circumferences have the same ratio as their radii.*

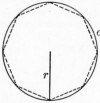 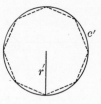

Given the circles with circumferences c and c', and radii r and r' respectively.

To prove that $c : c' = r : r'$.

Proof. Inscribe in the circles two similar regular polygons, and denote their perimeters by p and p'.

Then $p : p' = r : r'$.   § 375

Conceive the number of sides of these regular polygons to be indefinitely increased, the polygons continuing similar.

     Then p and p' will have c and c' as limits.   § 381

But the ratio $p : p'$ will always be equal to the ratio $r : r'$.   § 375

$$\therefore pr' = p'r. \qquad\qquad \text{§ 261}$$

$$\therefore cr' = c'r. \qquad\qquad \text{§ 207}$$

$$\therefore c : c' = r : r', \text{ by § 264.} \qquad \text{Q. E. D.}$$

383. COROLLARY 1. *The ratio of any circle to its diameter is constant.*

Why does $c : c' = 2\,r : 2\,r'$? Then why does $c : 2\,r = c' : 2\,r'$?

384. The Symbol π. The constant ratio of a circle to its diameter is represented by the Greek letter π (pī).

385. COROLLARY 2. *In any circle $c = 2\,\pi r$.*

For, by definition, $\pi = \dfrac{c}{2\,r}$.

PROPOSITION VIII. THEOREM

386. *The area of a regular polygon is equal to half the product of its apothem by its perimeter.*

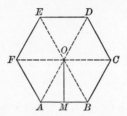

Given the regular polygon *ABCDEF*, **with apothem** *a*, **perimeter** *p*, **and area** *s*.

To prove that $s = \frac{1}{2} ap.$

Proof. Draw the radii OA, OB, OC, etc., to the successive vertices of the polygon.

The polygon is then divided into as many triangles as it has sides.

The apothem is the common altitude of these △, and the area of each △ is equal to $\frac{1}{2} a$ multiplied by the base.   § 325

Hence the area of all the triangles is equal to $\frac{1}{2} a$ multiplied by the sum of all the bases.   Ax. 1

But the sum of the areas of all the triangles is equal to the area of the polygon.   Ax. 11

And the sum of all the bases of the triangles is equal to the perimeter of the polygon.   Ax. 11

$$\therefore s = \frac{1}{2} ap.$$ Q. E. D.

387. Similar Parts. In different circles *similar arcs*, *similar sectors*, and *similar segments* are such arcs, sectors, and segments as correspond to equal angles at the center.

For example, two arcs of 30° in different circles are similar arcs, and the corresponding sectors are similar sectors.

PROPOSITION IX. THEOREM

388. *The area of a circle is equal to half the product of its radius by its circumference.*

Given a circle with radius r, circumference c, and area s.

To prove that $\qquad\qquad s = \frac{1}{2} rc$.

Proof. Circumscribe any regular polygon of n sides, and denote the perimeter of this polygon by p and its area by s'.

Then since r is its apothem, $s' = \frac{1}{2} rp$.   § 386

Conceive n to be indefinitely increased.

Then since p approaches c as its limit,   § 381

and r is constant,

$\therefore \frac{1}{2} rp$ approaches $\frac{1}{2} rc$ as its limit.

Also s' approaches s as its limit.   § 381

But $s' = \frac{1}{2} rp$ always.   § 386

$\therefore s = \frac{1}{2} rc$, by § 207.   Q. E. D.

389. COROLLARY 1. *The area of a circle is equal to π times the square on its radius.*

For the area of the $\odot = \frac{1}{2} rc = \frac{1}{2} r \times 2\pi r = \pi r^2$.

390. COROLLARY 2. *The areas of two circles are to each other as the squares on their radii.*

391. COROLLARY 3. *The area of a sector is equal to half the product of its radius by its arc.*

For $\dfrac{\text{area of sector}}{\text{area of circle}} = \dfrac{\text{arc of sector}}{\text{circle}}$.

EXERCISE 61

1. Two circles are constructed with radii $1\frac{1}{32}$ in. and $4\frac{1}{8}$ in. respectively. The circumference of the second is how many times that of the first?

2. The circumference of one circle is three times that of another. The square on the radius of the first is how many times the square on the radius of the second?

3. The circumference of one circle is $2\frac{1}{2}$ times that of another. The equilateral triangle constructed on the diameter of the first has how many times the area of the equilateral triangle constructed on the diameter of the second?

4. A circle with a diameter of 5 in. has a circumference of 15.708 in. What is the circumference of a pipe that has a diameter of 2 in.?

5. A wheel with a circumference of 4 ft. has a diameter of 1.27 ft., expressed to two decimal places. What is the circumference of a wheel with a diameter of $1.58\frac{3}{4}$ ft.?

6. A regular hexagon is 2 in. on a side. Find its apothem and its area to two decimal places.

7. An equilateral triangle is 2 in. on a side. Find its apothem and its area to two decimal places.

8. The radius of one circle is $2\frac{1}{2}$ times that of another. The area of the smaller is 15.2 sq. in. What is the area of the larger?

9. The radius of one circle is $3\frac{1}{4}$ times that of another. The area of the smaller is 17.75 sq. in. What is the area of the larger?

10. The circumferences of two cylindrical steel shafts are respectively 3 in. and $1\frac{1}{4}$ in. The area of a cross section of the first is how many times that of a cross section of the second?

11. The arc of a sector of a circle $2\frac{1}{4}$ in. in diameter is $1\frac{3}{4}$ in. What is the area of the sector?

Proposition X. Problem

392. *To inscribe a square in a given circle.*

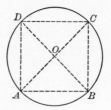

Given a circle with center O.

Required to inscribe a square in the given circle.

Construction. Draw two diameters AC and BD perpendicular to each other. § 228

Draw AB, BC, CD, and DA.

Then $ABCD$ is the square required. Q.E.F.

Proof. The $\angle s\ CBA$, DCB, ADC, BAD are rt. $\angle s$. § 215

(*An $\angle$ inscribed in a semicircle is a rt. $\angle$.*)

The $\angle s$ at the center O being rt. $\angle s$, Const.

the arcs AB, BC, CD, and DA are equal, § 212

and the sides AB, BC, CD, and DA are equal. § 170

Hence the quadrilateral $ABCD$ is a square, by § 65. Q.E.D.

393. Corollary. *To inscribe regular polygons of* 8, 16, 32, 64, *etc., sides in a given circle.*

By bisecting the arcs AB, BC, etc., a regular polygon of how many sides may be inscribed in the circle ? By continuing the process regular polygons of how many sides may be inscribed ?

In general we may say that this corollary allows us to inscribe a regular polygon of 2^n sides, where n is any positive integer. As a special case it is interesting to note that n may equal 1.

Proposition XI. Problem

394. *To inscribe a regular hexagon in a given circle.*

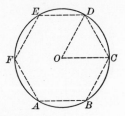

Given a circle with center *O*.

Required to inscribe a regular hexagon in the given circle.

Construction. From the center *O* draw any radius, as *OC*.

With *C* as a center, and a radius equal to *OC*, describe an arc intersecting the circle at *D*.

Draw *OD* and *CD*.

Then *CD* is a side of the regular hexagon required, and therefore the hexagon may be inscribed by applying *CD* six times as a chord.   Q. E. F.

Proof.   The △ *OCD* is equiangular.   § 75

(*An equilateral triangle is equiangular.*)

Hence the ∠ *COD* is $\frac{1}{3}$ of 2 rt. ∡, or $\frac{1}{6}$ of 4 rt. ∡.   § 107

∴ the arc *CD* is $\frac{1}{6}$ of the circle.

∴ the chord *CD* is a side of a regular inscribed hexagon. Q. E. D.

395. Corollary 1. *To inscribe an equilateral triangle in a given circle.*

By joining the alternate vertices of a regular inscribed hexagon, an equilateral triangle may be inscribed.

396. Corollary 2. *To inscribe regular polygons of* 12, 24, 48, *etc., sides in a given circle.*

Proposition XII. Problem

397. *To inscribe a regular decagon in a given circle.*

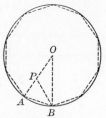

Given a circle with center O.

Required to inscribe a regular decagon in the given circle.

Construction.   Draw any radius OA,

and divide it in extreme and mean ratio,   § 311

so that $OA : OP = OP : AP$.

From A as a center, with a radius equal to OP,

describe an arc intersecting the circle at B.

Draw AB.

Then AB is a side of the regular decagon required, and therefore the regular decagon may be inscribed by applying AB ten times as a chord.   Q. E. F.

Proof.   Draw PB and OB.

Then $OA : OP = OP : AP$,   Const.

and $AB = OP$.   Const.

$\therefore OA : AB = AB : AP$.   Ax. 9

Moreover, $\angle BAO = \angle BAP$.   Iden.

Hence the $\triangle OAB$ and BAP are similar.   § 288

But the $\triangle OAB$ is isosceles.   § 162

$\therefore \triangle BAP$, which is similar to $\triangle OAB$, is isosceles,   § 282

and $AB = BP = OP$.   § 62

The $\triangle PBO$ being isosceles, the $\angle O = \angle OBP$.   § 74

But the $\angle APB = \angle O + \angle OBP = 2 \angle O.$ § 111

Hence $\angle BAP = 2 \angle O,$

and $\angle OBA = 2 \angle O.$ Ax. 9

$\therefore$ the sum of the $\angle\!\!\!\angle$ of the $\triangle OAB = 5 \angle O = 2$ rt. $\angle\!\!\!\angle$,   § 107

and $\angle O = \frac{1}{5}$ of 2 rt. $\angle\!\!\!\angle$, or $\frac{1}{10}$ of 4 rt. $\angle\!\!\!\angle$.   Ax. 4

Therefore the arc AB is $\frac{1}{10}$ of the circle.   § 212

$\therefore$ the chord AB is a side of a regular inscribed decagon.   Q.E.D.

398. COROLLARY 1. *To inscribe a regular pentagon in a given circle.*

399. COROLLARY 2. *To inscribe regular polygons of* 20, 40, 80, *etc., sides in a given circle.*

By bisecting the arcs subtended by the sides of a regular inscribed decagon a regular polygon of how many sides may be inscribed? By continuing the process regular polygons of how many sides may be inscribed?

EXERCISE 62

If r denotes the radius of a regular inscribed polygon, a the apothem, s one side, A an angle, and C the angle at the center, show that :

1. In a regular inscribed triangle $s = r\sqrt{3}$, $a = \frac{1}{2}r$, $A = 60°$, $C = 120°$.

2. In a regular inscribed quadrilateral $s = r\sqrt{2}$, $a = \frac{1}{2}r\sqrt{2}$, $A = 90°$, $C = 90°$.

3. In a regular inscribed hexagon $s = r$, $a = \frac{1}{2}r\sqrt{3}$, $A = 120°$, $C = 60°$.

4. In a regular inscribed decagon

$$s = \frac{r(\sqrt{5}-1)}{2}, \quad a = \frac{1}{4}r\sqrt{10 + 2\sqrt{5}}, \quad A = 144°, \quad C = 36°.$$

Proposition XIII. Problem

400. *To inscribe in a given circle a regular pentadec-agon, or polygon of fifteen sides.*

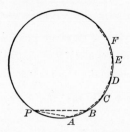

Given a circle.

Required to inscribe a regular pentadecagon in the given circle.

Construction. Draw a chord PB equal to the radius of the circle, a chord PA equal to a side of the regular inscribed decagon, and draw AB.

Then AB is a side of the regular pentadecagon required, and therefore the regular pentadecagon may be inscribed by apply-ing AB fifteen times as a chord.   Q. E. F.

Proof.   The arc PB is $\frac{1}{6}$ of the circle,   § 394

and the arc PA is $\frac{1}{10}$ of the circle.   § 397

Hence the arc AB is $\frac{1}{6} - \frac{1}{10}$, or $\frac{1}{15}$, of the circle.   Ax. 2

Therefore the chord AB is a side of the regular inscribed pentadecagon required.   Q. E. D.

401. Corollary. *To inscribe regular polygons of 30, 60, 120, etc., sides in a given circle.*

By bisecting the arcs AB, BC, etc., a regular polygon of how many sides may be inscribed? By continuing the process regular polygons of how many sides may be inscribed? In general we may say that a regular polygon of $15 \cdot 2^n$ sides may be inscribed in this manner.

EXERCISE 63

1. A five-cent piece is placed on the table. How many five-cent pieces can be placed around it, each tangent to it and tangent to two of the others? Prove it.

2. What is the perimeter of an equilateral triangle inscribed in a circle with radius 1 in.?

3. What is the perimeter of an equilateral triangle circumscribed about a circle with radius 1 in.?

4. What is the perimeter of a regular hexagon circumscribed about a circle with radius 1 in.?

Required to circumscribe about a given circle the following regular polygons:

    5. Triangle.   **7.** Hexagon.   **9.** Pentagon.

    6. Quadrilateral.   **8.** Octagon.   **10.** Decagon.

11. Required to describe a circle whose circumference equals the sum of the circumferences of two circles of given radii.

12. Required to describe a circle whose area equals the sum of the areas of two circles of given radii.

13. Required to describe a circle having three times the area of a given circle.

Required to construct an angle of:

14. 18°.   **15.** 36°.   **16.** 9°.   **17.** 12°.   **18.** 24°.

Required to construct with a side of given length:

    19. An equilateral triangle.   **23.** A regular pentagon.

    20. A square.   **24.** A regular decagon.

    21. A regular hexagon.   **25.** A regular dodecagon.

    22. A regular octagon.   **26.** A regular pentadecagon.

27. From a circular log 16 in. in diameter a builder wishes to cut a column with its cross section as large a regular octagon as possible. Find the length of each side.

Proposition XIV. Problem

402. *Given the side and the radius of a regular inscribed polygon, to find the side of the regular inscribed polygon of double the number of sides.*

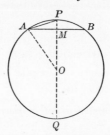

Given *AB*, the side of a regular inscribed polygon of radius *OA*.

Required to find AP, a side of the regular inscribed polygon of double the number of sides.

Solution. Denote the radius by r, and the side AB by s.

Draw the diameter $PQ \perp$ to AB, and draw AO and AQ.

Then	$AM = \frac{1}{2}s.$	§ 174
In the rt. $\triangle AOM$,	$\overline{OM}^2 = r^2 - \frac{1}{4}s^2.$	§ 338
Therefore	$OM = \sqrt{r^2 - \frac{1}{4}s^2}.$	Ax. 5
Since	$PM + OM = r,$	Ax. 11
therefore	$PM = r - OM$	Ax. 2
	$= r - \sqrt{r^2 - \frac{1}{4}s^2}.$	Ax. 9
Furthermore	$\overline{AP}^2 = PQ \times PM.$	§ 298

But $PQ = 2\,r$, and $PM = r - \sqrt{r^2 - \frac{1}{4}s^2}.$

$$\therefore \overline{AP}^2 = 2\,r\left(r - \sqrt{r^2 - \tfrac{1}{4}s^2}\right). \qquad \text{Ax. 9}$$

$$\therefore AP = \sqrt{2\,r\left(r - \sqrt{r^2 - \tfrac{1}{4}s^2}\right)} \qquad \text{Ax. 5}$$

$$= \sqrt{r\left(2\,r - \sqrt{4\,r^2 - s^2}\right)}. \qquad \text{Q.E.F.}$$

403. Corollary. *If* $r = 1$, $AP = \sqrt{2 - \sqrt{4 - s^2}}.$

Proposition XV. Problem

404. *To find the numerical value of the ratio of the circumference of a circle to its diameter.*

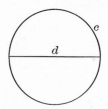

Given a circle of circumference *c* and diameter *d*.

Required to find the numerical value of $\dfrac{c}{d}$ or π.

Solution. By § 385, $2\pi r = c$. $\therefore \pi = \frac{1}{2}c$ when $r = 1$.

Let s_6 (read "*s* sub six") be the length of a side of a regular polygon of 6 sides, s_{12} of 12 sides, and so on.

If $r = 1$, by § 394, $s_6 = 1$, and by § 403 we have

Form of Computation	Length of Side	Length of Perimeter
$s_{12} = \sqrt{2 - \sqrt{4 - 1^2}}$	0.51763809	6.21165708
$s_{24} = \sqrt{2 - \sqrt{4 - (0.51763809)^2}}$	0.26105238	6.26525722
$s_{48} = \sqrt{2 - \sqrt{4 - (0.26105238)^2}}$	0.13080626	6.27870041
$s_{96} = \sqrt{2 - \sqrt{4 - (0.13080626)^2}}$	0.06543817	6.28206396
$s_{192} = \sqrt{2 - \sqrt{4 - (0.06543817)^2}}$	0.03272346	6.28290510
$s_{384} = \sqrt{2 - \sqrt{4 - (0.03272346)^2}}$	0.01636228	6.28311544
$s_{768} = \sqrt{2 - \sqrt{4 - (0.01636228)^2}}$	0.00818121	6.28316941

$\therefore c = 6.28317$ nearly ; that is, $\pi = 3.14159$ nearly.   Q. E. F

π is an incommensurable number. We generally take

$$\pi = 3.1416, \text{ or } 3\tfrac{1}{7}, \text{ and } \frac{1}{\pi} = 0.31831.$$

EXERCISE 64

PROBLEMS OF COMPUTATION

Using the value 3.1416 for π, find the circumferences of circles with radii as follows:

1. 3 in.   **3.** 2.7 in.   **5.** $7\frac{1}{2}$ in.   **7.** 2 ft. 8 in.

2. 5 in.   **4.** 3.4 in.   **6.** $6\frac{3}{4}$ in.   **8.** 3 ft. 7 in.

Find the circumferences of circles with diameters as follows:

9. 9 in.   **11.** 5.9 in.   **13.** $2\frac{1}{2}$ ft.   **15.** 29 centimeters.

10. 12 in.   **12.** 7.3 in.   **14.** $3\frac{1}{8}$ in.   **16.** 47 millimeters.

Find the radii of circles with circumferences as follows:

17. 7π.   **19.** 15.708 in.   **21.** 18.8496 in.   **23.** 345.576 ft.

18. $3\frac{1}{3}\pi$.   **20.** 21.9912 in.   **22.** 125.664 in.   **24.** 3487.176 in.

Find the diameters of circles with circumferences as follows:

25. 15π.   **27.** $2\pi r$.   **29.** 188.496 in.   **31.** 3361.512 in.

26. π^2.   **28.** $7\pi a^2$.   **30.** 219.912 in.   **32.** 3173.016 in.

Find the areas of circles with radii as follows:

33. $5x$.   **35.** 27 ft.   **37.** $3\frac{1}{8}$ in.   **39.** 2 ft. 6 in.

34. 2π.   **36.** 4.8 ft.   **38.** $4\frac{5}{8}$ in.   **40.** 7 ft. 9 in.

Find the areas of circles with diameters as follows:

41. $16\,ab$.   **43.** 2.5 ft.   **45.** $3\frac{2}{3}$ yd.   **47.** 3 ft. 2 in.

42. $24\,\pi^2$.   **44.** 7.3 in.   **46.** $4\frac{5}{8}$ yd.   **48.** 4 ft. 1 in.

Find the areas of circles with circumferences as follows:

49. 2π.   **51.** πa.   **53.** 18.8496 in.   **55.** 333.0096 in.

50. 4π.   **52.** $14\pi a^2$.   **54.** 329.868 in.   **56.** 364.4256 in.

Find the radii of circles with areas as follows:

57. $\pi a^2 b^4$.   **59.** π.   **61.** 12.5664.   **63.** 78.54.

58. $4\pi m^4 n^6$.   **60.** 2π.   **62.** 28.2744.   **64.** 113.0976.

EXERCISE 65

PROBLEMS OF CONSTRUCTION

1. To inscribe in a given circle a regular polygon similar to a given regular polygon.

2. To divide by a concentric circle the area of a given circle into two equivalent parts.

3. To divide by concentric circles the area of a given circle into n equivalent parts.

4. To describe a circle whose circumference is equal to the difference of two circumferences of given radii.

5. To describe a circle the ratio of whose area to that of a given circle shall be equal to the given ratio $m : n$.

6. To construct a regular pentagon, given one of the diagonals.

7. To draw a tangent to a given circle such that the segment intercepted between the point of contact and a given line shall have a given length.

8. In a given equilateral triangle to inscribe three equal circles tangent each to the other two, each circle being tangent to two sides of the triangle.

9. In a given square to inscribe four equal circles, so that each circle shall be tangent to two of the others and also tangent to two sides of the square.

10. In a given square to inscribe four equal circles, so that each circle shall be tangent to two of the others and also tangent to one side and only one side of the square.

11. To draw a common secant to two given circles exterior to each other, such that the intercepted chords shall have the given lengths a and b.

12. To draw through a point of intersection of two given intersecting circles a common secant of a given length.

EXERCISE 66

PROBLEMS OF LOCI

1. Find the locus of the center of the circle inscribed in a triangle that has a given base and a given angle at the vertex.

2. Find the locus of the intersection of the perpendiculars from the three vertices to the opposite sides of a triangle that has a given base and a given angle at the vertex.

3. Find the locus of the extremity of a tangent to a given circle, if the length of the tangent is equal to a given line.

4. Find the locus of a point from which tangents drawn to a given circle form a given angle.

5. Find the locus of the mid-point of a line drawn from a given point to a given line.

6. Find the locus of the vertex of a triangle that has a given base and a given altitude.

7. Find the locus of a point the sum of whose distances from two given parallel lines is constant.

8. Find the locus of a point the difference of whose distances from two given parallel lines is constant.

9. Find the locus of a point the sum of whose distances from two given intersecting lines is constant.

10. Find the locus of a point the difference of whose distances from two given intersecting lines is constant.

11. Find the locus of a point whose distances from two given points are in the ratio $m : n$.

12. Find the locus of a point whose distances from two given parallel lines are in the ratio $m : n$.

13. Find the locus of a point whose distances from two given intersecting lines are in the ratio $m : n$.

14. Find the locus of a point the sum of the squares of whose distances from two given points is constant.

EXERCISE 67

EXAMINATION QUESTIONS

1. Each side of a triangle is $2n$ centimeters, and about each vertex as a center, with a radius of n centimeters, a circle is described. Find the area bounded by the three arcs that lie outside the triangle, and the area bounded by the three arcs that lie within the triangle.

2. Upon a line AB a segment of a circle containing 240° is constructed, and in the segment any chord CD subtending an arc of 60° is drawn. Find the locus of the intersection of AC and BD, and also of the intersection of AD and BC.

3. Three successive vertices of a regular octagon are A, B, and C. If the length AB is a, compute the length AC.

4. The areas of similar segments of circles are proportional to the squares on their radii.

5. An arc of a certain circle is 100 ft. long and subtends an angle of 25° at the center. Compute the radius of the circle correct to one decimal place.

6. Given a circle whose radius is 16, find the perimeter and the area of the regular inscribed octagon.

7. If two circles intersect at the points A and B, and through A a variable secant is drawn, cutting the circles in C and D, the angle CBD is constant for all positions of the secant.

8. If A and B are two fixed points on a given circle, and P and Q are the extremities of a variable diameter of the same circle, find the locus of the point of intersection of the lines AP and BQ.

9. The radius of a circle is 10 ft. Two parallel chords are drawn, each equal to the radius. Find that part of the area of the circle lying between the parallel chords.

The propositions in Exercise 67 are taken from recent college entrance examination papers.

FORMULAS

If r denotes the radius of a circle, and s one side of a regular inscribed polygon, prove the following, and find the value of s to two decimal places when $r = 1$:

1. In an equilateral triangle $s = r\sqrt{3}$.

2. In a square $s = r\sqrt{2}$.

3. In a regular pentagon $s = \frac{1}{2}r\sqrt{10 - 2\sqrt{5}}$.

4. In a regular hexagon $s = r$.

5. In a regular octagon $s = r\sqrt{2 - \sqrt{2}}$.

6. In a regular decagon $s = \frac{1}{2}r(\sqrt{5} - 1)$.

7. In a regular dodecagon $s = r\sqrt{2 - \sqrt{3}}$.

8. A regular pentagon is inscribed in a circle whose radius is r. If the side is s, find the apothem.

9. A regular polygon is inscribed in a circle whose radius is r. If the side is s, show that the apothem is $\frac{1}{2}\sqrt{4r^2 - s^2}$.

10. If the radius of a circle is r, and the side of an inscribed regular polygon is s, show that the side of the similar circumscribed regular polygon is $\dfrac{2sr}{\sqrt{4r^2 - s^2}}$.

11. Three equal circles are described, each tangent to the other two. If the common radius is r, find the area contained between the circles.

12. Given p, P, the perimeters of regular polygons of n sides inscribed in and circumscribed about a given circle. Find p', P', the perimeters of regular polygons of $2n$ sides inscribed in and circumscribed about the given circle.

13. A circular plot of land d ft. in diameter is surrounded by a walk w ft. wide. Find the area of the circular plot and the area of the walk.

EXERCISE 69

Applied Problems

1. The diameter of a bicycle wheel is 28 in. How many revolutions does the wheel make in going 10 mi. ?

2. Find the diameter of a carriage wheel that makes 264 revolutions in going half a mile.

3. A circular pond 100 yd. in diameter is surrounded by a walk 10 ft. wide. Find the area of the walk.

4. The span (chord) of a bridge in the form of a circular arc is 120 ft., and the highest point of the arch is 15 ft. above the piers. Find the radius of the arc.

5. Two branch water pipes lead into a main pipe. It is necessary that the cross-section area of the main pipe shall equal the sum of the cross sections of the two branch pipes. The diameters of the branch pipes are respectively 3 in. and 4 in. Required the diameter of the main pipe.

6. A kite is made as here shown, the semicircle having a radius of 9 in., and the triangle a height of 25 in. Find the area of the kite.

7. In making a drawing for an arch it is required to mark off on a circle drawn with a radius of 5 in. an arc that shall be 8 in. long. This is best done by finding the angle at the center. How many degrees are there in this angle ?

8. In an iron washer here shown, the diameter of the hole is $1\frac{3}{8}$ in. and the width of the washer is $\frac{3}{8}$ in. Find the area of one face of the washer.

9. Find the area of a fan that opens out into a sector of 120°, the radius being $9\frac{3}{8}$ in.

10. The area of a fan that opens out into a sector of 111° is 96.866 sq. in. What is the radius ? (Take $\pi = 3.1416$.)

EXERCISE 70

REVIEW QUESTIONS

1. What is meant by a regular polygon? by its radius? by its center? by its apothem?

2. What other names are there for a regular triangle and a regular quadrilateral?

3. If one angle of a regular polygon is known, how can the number of sides be determined?

4. The sides of two regular polygons of n sides are respectively s and s'. What is the ratio of their radii? of their apothems? of their perimeters? of their areas?

5. The diameters of two circles are d and d' respectively. What is the ratio of their radii? of their circumferences? of their areas?

6. If the number of sides of a regular inscribed polygon is indefinitely increased, what is the limit of the apothem? of each side? of the perimeter? of the area? of the angle at the center? of each angle of the polygon?

7. How do you find the area of a regular polygon? of an irregular polygon? of a square? of a triangle? of a parallelogram? of a circle? of a trapezoid? of a sector?

8. What regular polygons have you learned to inscribe in a circle? Name three regular polygons that you have not learned to inscribe.

9. Given the circumference of a circle, how can the area of the circle be found?

10. Given the area of a circle, how can the circumference of the circle be found?

11. What is the radius of the circle of which the number of linear units of circumference is equal to the number of square units of area?

EXERCISE 71

General Review of Plane Geometry

Write a classification of the different kinds of:

1. Lines.	**3.** Triangles.	**5.** Polygons.
2. Angles.	**4.** Quadrilaterals.	**6.** Parallelograms.

State the conditions under which:

7. Two triangles are congruent.

8. Two parallelograms are congruent.

9. Two triangles are similar.

10. Two straight lines are parallel.

11. Two parallelograms are equivalent.

12. Two polygons are similar.

Complete the following statements in the most general manner:

13. In any triangle the square on the side opposite ⋅ ⋅.

14. If two parallel lines are cut by a transversal, ⋯

15. If four quantities are in proportion, they are in proportion by ⋯.

16. If two secants of a circle intersect, the angle formed is measured by ⋯.

17. The perimeters of two similar polygons are to each other as ⋯.

18. The areas of two similar polygons are to each other as ⋯.

19. The area of a circle is equal to ⋯.

20. In the same circle or in equal circles equal chords ⋯.

21. In the same circle or in equal circles the central angles subtended by two arcs are ⋯.

22. If two secants of a circle intersect within, on, or outside the circle, the product of ⋯.

23. If four lines meet in a point so that the opposite angles are equal, these lines form two intersecting straight lines.

24. If squares are constructed outwardly on the six sides of a regular hexagon, the exterior vertices of these squares are the vertices of a regular dodecagon.

25. In a right triangle the line joining the vertex of the right angle to the mid-point of the hypotenuse is equal to half the hypotenuse.

26. No two lines drawn from the vertices of the base angles of a triangle to the opposite sides can bisect each other.

27. The rhombus is the only parallelogram that can be circumscribed about a circle.

28. The square is the only rectangle that can be circumscribed about a circle.

29. No oblique parallelogram can be inscribed in a circle.

30. If two triangles have equal bases and equal vertical angles, the two circumscribing circles have equal diameters.

31. If the inscribed and circumscribed circles of a triangle are concentric, the triangle is equilateral.

32. If the three points of contact of a circle inscribed in a triangle are joined, the angles of the resulting triangle are all acute.

33. The diagonals of a regular pentagon intersect at the vertices of another regular pentagon.

34. If two perpendicular radii of a circle are produced to intersect a tangent to the circle, the other tangents from the two points of intersection are parallel.

35. The line that joins the feet of the perpendiculars drawn from the extremities of the base of an isosceles triangle to the equal sides is parallel to the base.

36. The sum of the perpendiculars drawn to the sides of a regular polygon from any point within the polygon is equal to the apothem multiplied by the number of sides.

37. If two consecutive angles of a quadrilateral are right angles, the bisectors of the other two angles are perpendicular.

38. If two opposite angles of a quadrilateral are right angles, the bisectors of the other two angles are parallel.

39. The two lines that join the mid-points of opposite sides of a quadrilateral bisect each other.

40. The sum of the angles at the vertices of a five-pointed star is equal to two right angles.

41. The segments of any line intercepted between two concentric circles are equal.

42. The diagonals of a trapezoid divide each other into segments which are proportional.

43. Given the mid-points of the sides of a triangle, to construct the triangle.

44. To divide a given triangle into two equivalent parts by a line through one of the vertices.

45. To draw a tangent to a given circle that shall also be perpendicular to a given line.

46. To divide a given line into two segments such that the square on one shall be double the square on the other.

47. If any two consecutive sides of an inscribed hexagon are respectively parallel to their opposite sides, the remaining two sides are parallel.

48. If through any given point in the common chord of two intersecting circles two other chords are drawn, one in each circle, their four extremities will all lie on a third circle.

49. If two chords intersect at right angles within a circle, the sum of the squares on their segments equals the square on the diameter. Investigate the case in which the chords intersect outside the circle; also the case in which they intersect on the circle.

50. The lines bisecting any angle of an inscribed quadrilateral and the opposite exterior angle intersect on the circle.

51. The sum of the perpendiculars from any point in an equilateral triangle to the three sides is constant.

52. The perpendiculars from the vertices of a triangle upon the opposite sides cut one another into segments that are reciprocally proportional to each other.

53. The area of a triangle is equal to half the product of its perimeter by the radius of the inscribed circle.

54. The perimeter of a triangle is to one side as the perpendicular from the opposite vertex is to the radius of the inscribed circle.

55. The area of a square inscribed in a semicircle is equal to two fifths of the area of the square inscribed in the circle.

56. The diagonals of any inscribed quadrilateral divide it into two pairs of similar triangles.

57. To draw a line whose length is $\sqrt{7\frac{1}{2}}$ in.

58. If two equivalent triangles are on the same base and the same side of the base, any line cutting the triangles, and parallel to the base, cuts off equal areas from the triangles.

59. To divide a given arc of a circle into two parts such that their chords shall be in a given ratio.

60. The area between two concentric circles may be found by multiplying half the sum of the two circumferences by the difference between the radii.

61. Find the length of the belt connecting two wheels of the same size, if the radius of each wheel is 18 in., the distance between the centers 6 ft., and 4 in. is allowed for sagging.

62. To construct a regular inscribed heptagon draftsmen sometimes use for a side half the side of an inscribed equilateral triangle. Construct such a figure with the compasses, and state whether the rule seems exact or only approximate.

APPENDIX

405. Subjects Treated. Of the many additional subjects that may occupy the attention of the student of plane geometry if time permits, two are of special interest. These are Symmetry, and Maxima and Minima.

406. Symmetric Points. Two points are said to be *symmetric with respect to a point*, called the *center of symmetry*, if this third point bisects the straight line which joins the two points.

Two points are said to be *symmetric with respect to an axis*, if a straight line, called the *axis of symmetry*, is the perpendicular bisector of the line joining them.

407. Symmetric Figure. A figure is said to be *symmetric with respect to a point*, if the point bisects every straight line drawn through it and terminated by the boundary of the figure.

A figure is said to be *symmetric with respect to an axis*, if the axis bisects every perpendicular through it and terminated by the boundary of the figure.

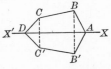

Evidently this will be the case if one part coincides with another part when folded over the axis.

408. Two Symmetric Figures. Two figures are said to be *symmetric with respect to a point* or *symmetric with respect to an axis*, if every point of each has a corresponding symmetric point in the other.

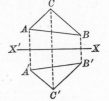

261

Proposition I. Theorem

409. *A quadrilateral that has two adjacent sides equal, and the other two sides equal, is symmetric with respect to the diagonal joining the vertices of the angles formed by the equal sides; and the diagonals are perpendicular to each other.*

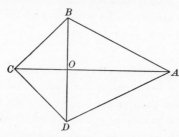

Given the quadrilateral *ABCD*, having *AB* equal to *AD*, and *CB* equal to *CD*, and having the diagonals *AC* and *BD*.

To prove that the diagonal AC is an axis of symmetry, and that AC is ⊥ *to BD.*

Proof. In the △ *ABC* and *ADC*,

$$AB = AD, \text{ and } CB = CD, \qquad \text{Given}$$

and
$$AC = AC. \qquad \text{Iden.}$$

∴ △ *ABC* is congruent to △ *ADC*.   § 80

∴ ∠ *BAC* = ∠ *CAD*, and ∠ *ACB* = ∠ *DCA*.   § 67

Hence, if △ *ABC* is turned on *AC* as an axis until it falls on △ *ADC*, *AB* will fall on *AD*, *CB* on *CD*, and *OB* on *OD*.

∴ the △ *ABC* will coincide with the △ *ADC*.

∴ *AC* will bisect every perpendicular drawn through it and terminated by the boundary of the figure.

∴ *AC* is an axis of symmetry.   § 407

∴ *AC* is ⊥ to *BD*, by § 406.   Q. E. D.

Proposition II. Theorem

410. *If a figure is symmetric with respect to two axes perpendicular to each other, it is symmetric with respect to their intersection as a center.*

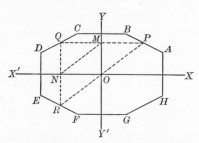

Given the figure *ABCDEFGH*, symmetric with respect to the two perpendicular axes *XX′*, *YY′*, which intersect at *O*.

To prove that O is the center of symmetry of the figure.

Proof.   Let *P* be any point in the perimeter.

Draw $PMQ \perp$ to *YY′*, and $QNR \perp$ to *XX′*.   § 227

Then   *PQ* is ∥ to *XX′*, and *QR* is ∥ to *YY′*.   § 95

Draw *PO*, *OR*, and *MN*.

Then $QN = NR$.   § 407

(The figure is given as symmetric with respect to XX′.)

But $QN = MO$.   § 127

∴ $NR = MO$.   Ax. 8

∴ *RO* is equal and parallel to *NM*.   § 130

In like manner, *OP* is equal and parallel to *NM*.

∴ *ROP* is a straight line.   § 94

∴ *O* bisects *PR*, any straight line, and hence bisects every straight line drawn through *O* and terminated by the perimeter.

∴ *O* is the center of symmetry of the figure, by § 407.   Q.E.D.

1. Draw a figure showing the number of axes of symmetry possessed by a square.

2. Draw a figure showing the number of axes of symmetry possessed by a regular hexagon.

3. Draw a figure showing six of the unlimited number of axes of symmetry of a circle, and showing the center of symmetry.

4. Show by drawings that two congruent triangles may be placed in a position of symmetry with respect to an axis. In one of the drawings let a common side be the axis.

5. Show by a drawing that two congruent triangles may be placed in a position of symmetry with respect to a center.

6. Two figures symmetric with respect to an axis are congruent.

7. Two figures symmetric with respect to a center are congruent.

8. Make a list of quadrilaterals that are symmetric with respect to an axis.

9. Make a list of quadrilaterals that are symmetric with respect to a center.

10. What kinds of regular polygons are symmetric with respect both to a center and to an axis? Prove this for the hexagon.

11. A circle is symmetric with respect to its center as a center of symmetry, and is also symmetric with respect to any diameter as an axis.

12. An isosceles triangle is symmetric with respect to an axis, and therefore the angles opposite the equal sides are equal.

13. Two tangents drawn to a circle from the same point are symmetric with respect to an axis.

14. The four common tangents to two given circles form, together with the circles, a figure symmetric with respect to the line of centers as an axis.

411. Maxima and Minima. Among geometric magnitudes that satisfy given conditions, the *greatest* is called the *maximum*, and the *smallest* is called the *minimum*.

The plural of maximum is *maxima*, and the plural of minimum is *minima*.

Among geometric magnitudes that satisfy given conditions, there may be several equal magnitudes that are greater than any others. In this case all are called maxima.

Similarly there may be several minima magnitudes of a given kind.

412. Isoperimetric Polygons. Polygons which have equal perimeters are called *isoperimetric polygons*.

If the circumference of a circle equals the perimeter of a polygon, the circle and the polygon are said to be isoperimetric, and similarly for all other closed figures in a plane.

PROPOSITION III. THEOREM

413. *Of all triangles having two given sides, that in which these sides include a right angle is the maximum.*

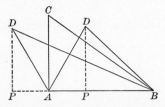

Given the triangles *ABC* and *ABD*, with *AB* and *CA* equal to *AB* and *DA* respectively, and with angle *BAC* a right angle.

To prove that $\triangle ABC > \triangle ABD$.

Proof.	From *D* draw the altitude *DP*.	§ 227
Then	$DA > DP$.	§ 86
But	$DA = CA$.	Given
	$\therefore CA > DP$.	Ax. 9
	$\therefore \triangle ABC > \triangle ABD$, by § 327.	Q.E D.

Proposition IV. Theorem

414. *Of all isoperimetric triangles having the same base the isosceles triangle is the maximum.*

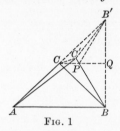 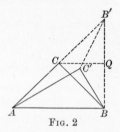

Fig. 1   Fig. 2

Given the triangles *ABC* and *ABC'* having equal perimeters, and having *AC* equal to *BC*, and *AC'* not equal to *BC'*.

To prove that $\triangle ABC > \triangle ABC'$.

Proof.   Produce *AC* to *B'*, making $CB' = AC$.

       Draw *BB'* and *C'B'*, and draw *CQ* ∥ to *AB*.

Then since $AC = CB'$, ∴ $BQ = QB'$.   § 135

And since $CA = CB = CB'$, ∴ ∠ *B'BA* is a rt. ∠.   § 215

             ∴ *CQ* is ⊥ to *BB'*.   § 97

C' cannot lie on *AB'*, for if it could, then $CC' + C'B$ would equal *CB*, which is impossible.   Post. 1

Then since $AC + CB' < AC' + C'B'$,   § 112

        ∴ $AC + CB < AC' + C'B'$.   Ax. 9

       ∴ $AC' + C'B < AC' + C'B'$.   Ax. 9

              ∴ $C'B < C'B'$.   Ax. 6

∴ *C'* cannot lie on *CQ*, for then *C'B* would equal *C'B'*.   § 150

C' cannot lie above *CQ* (Fig. 1), for *C'B'*, which $< C'P + PB'$, would be less than *C'B*, which equals $C'P + PB'$.

            ∴ *C'* must lie below *CQ*, as in Fig. 2.

            ∴ $\triangle ABC > \triangle ABC'$, by § 327.   Q. E. D.

PROPOSITION V. THEOREM

415. *Of all polygons with sides all given but one, the maximum can be inscribed in the semicircle which has the undetermined side for its diameter.*

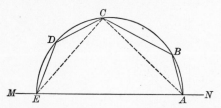

Given *ABCDE*, the maximum of polygons with sides *AB*, *BC*, *CD*, *DE*, having the vertices *A* and *E* on the line *MN*.

To prove that ABCDE can be inscribed in the semicircle having EA for its diameter.

Proof. From any vertex, as *C*, draw *CA* and *CE*.

The △ *ACE* must be the maximum of all △ having the sides *CA* and *CE*, and the third side on *MN*; otherwise, by increasing or diminishing the ∠ *ECA*, keeping the lengths of the sides *CA* and *CE* unchanged, but sliding the extremities *A* and *E* along the line *MN*, we could increase the △ *ACE*, while the rest of the polygon would remain unchanged; and therefore we could increase the polygon. But this is contrary to the hypothesis that the polygon is the maximum polygon.

Hence the △ *ACE* is the maximum of triangles that have the sides *CA* and *CE*.

Therefore the ∠ *ACE* is a right angle. § 413

Therefore *C* lies on the semicircle having *EA* for its diameter. § 215

Hence every vertex lies on this semicircle.

That is, the maximum polygon can be inscribed in the semicircle having the undetermined side for its diameter. Q.E.D.

Proposition VI. Theorem

416. *Of all polygons with given sides, one that can be inscribed in a circle is the maximum.*

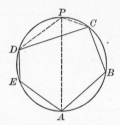 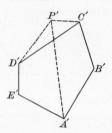

Given the polygon *ABCDE* inscribed in a circle, and the polygon *A'B'C'D'E'* which has its sides equal respectively to the sides of *ABCDE*, but which cannot be inscribed in a circle.

To prove that $ABCDE > A'B'C'D'E'$.

Proof. Draw the diameter AP, and draw CP and PD.

Upon $C'D'$ as a base, construct the $\triangle C'P'D'$ congruent to the $\triangle CPD$, and draw $A'P'$.

Since, by hypothesis, a $\odot$ cannot pass through all the vertices of $A'B'C'P'D'E'$, one or both of the parts $A'P'D'E'$, $A'B'C'P'$ cannot be inscribed in a semicircle.

Neither $A'P'D'E'$ or $A'B'C'P'$ can be greater than its corresponding part.   § 415

(Of all polygons with sides all given but one, the maximum can be inscribed in the semicircle which has the undetermined side for its diameter.)

Therefore one of the parts $A'P'D'E'$, $A'B'C'P'$ must be less than, and the other cannot be greater than, the corresponding part of $ABCPDE$.

$$\therefore ABCPDE > A'B'C'P'D'E'.$$

Take from the two figures the congruent $\triangle\!\!\!\triangle\ CPD$ and $C'P'D'$.

Then $ABCDE > A'B'C'D'E'$, by Ax. 6.   Q. E. D.

Proposition VII. Theorem

417. *Of isoperimetric polygons of a given number of sides, the maximum is equilateral.*

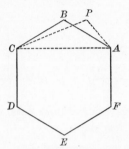

Given the polygon *ABCDEF*, the maximum of isoperimetric polygons of *n* sides.

To prove that the polygon ABCDEF is equilateral.

Proof.   Draw *AC*.

The △ *ABC* must be the maximum of all the △ which are formed upon *AC* with a perimeter equal to that of △ *ABC*.

Otherwise a greater △ *APC* could be substituted for △ *ABC*, without changing the perimeter of the polygon.

But this is inconsistent with the fact that the polygon *ABCDEF* is given as the maximum polygon.

∴ the △ *ABC* is isosceles.   § 414

∴ *AB = BC*.

Similarly   *BC = CD, CD = DE*, and so on.

∴ the polygon *ABCDEF* is equilateral.   Q.E.D.

418. Corollary. *The maximum of isoperimetric polygons of a given number of sides is a regular polygon.*

For the maximum polygon is equilateral (§ 417), and can be inscribed in a circle (§ 416). Therefore the maximum polygon is regular (§ 365).

Proposition VIII. Theorem

419. *Of isoperimetric regular polygons, that which has the greatest number of sides is the maximum.*

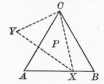

Given the regular polygon *P* of three sides, and the isoperimetric regular polygon *P'* of four sides.

To prove that $P' > P$.

Proof. Draw *CX* from *C* to any point *X* in *AB*.

Invert the $\triangle AXC$ and place it in the position *XCY*, letting *X* fall at *C*, *C* at *X*, and *A* at *Y*.

The polygon *XBCY* is an irregular polygon of four sides, which by construction has the same perimeter as *P'* and the same area as *P*.

Then the regular polygon *P'* of four sides is greater than the isoperimetric irregular polygon *XBCY* of four sides.   § 418

That is, a regular polygon of four sides is greater than the isoperimetric regular polygon of three sides.

In like manner, it may be shown that *P'* is less than the isoperimetric regular polygon of five sides, and so on.   Q.E.D.

Discussion. We may illustrate this by the case of an equilateral triangle and a square, each with the perimeter p. In the triangle the base is $\frac{1}{3} p$, the altitude $\frac{1}{6} p \sqrt{3}$, and the area $\frac{1}{36} p^2 \sqrt{3}$, or about $0.048\, p^2$. In the square the base and altitude are each $\frac{1}{4} p$, and the area is $\frac{1}{16} p^2$, or $0.0625\, p^2$. The area of the polygon is therefore increasing as we increase the number of sides.

Since the limit approached by the perimeters is a circle, we may infer that *of all isoperimetric plane figures the circle has the greatest area.*

PROPOSITION IX. THEOREM

420. *Of regular polygons having a given area, that which has the greatest number of sides has the minimum perimeter.*

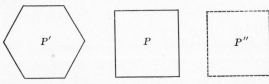

Given the regular polygons P and P' having the same area, P' having the greater number of sides.

To prove that the perimeter of $P >$ the perimeter of P'.

Proof. Construct the regular polygon P'' having the same perimeter as P', and the same number of sides as P.

Denote a side of P by s, and a side of P'' by s''.

Then	$P' > P''$.	§ 419
But	$P = P'$.	Given
	$\therefore P > P''$.	Ax. 9
But	$P : P'' = s^2 : s''^2$.	§ 374
	$\therefore s^2 > s''^2$.	
	$\therefore s > s''$.	Ax. 6

$\therefore$ the perimeter of $P >$ the perimeter of P''. Ax. 6

But the perimeter of $P' =$ the perimeter of P''. Const.

$\therefore$ the perimeter of $P >$ the perimeter of P', by Ax. 9. Q.E.D.

Discussion. We may illustrate this, as on page 270, by the case of an equilateral triangle and a square, each with area a^2. The side of the square is a, and the perimeter $4\,a$. The area of the equilateral triangle is $\frac{1}{4} s^2 \sqrt{3}$. Therefore $\frac{1}{4} s^2 \sqrt{3} = a^2$, or $\frac{1}{2} s \sqrt[4]{3} = a$. Now $\sqrt[4]{3} = \sqrt{\sqrt{3}}$; hence we have $\sqrt{3} = 1.73 +$, and $\sqrt{\sqrt{3}} = \sqrt{1.73} = 1.3 +$. Hence $\frac{1}{2} s \times 1.3 = a$, and $s = 1.5\,a$, and the perimeter of the triangle is $4.5\,a$. Therefore the perimeter of the square is less than that of the triangle.

EXERCISE 73

Maxima and Minima

1. Of all equivalent parallelograms that have equal bases, the rectangle has the minimum perimeter.

2. Of all equivalent rectangles, the square has the minimum perimeter.

3. Of all triangles that have the same base and the same altitude, the isosceles has the minimum perimeter.

4. Of all triangles that can be inscribed in a given circle, the equilateral is the maximum and has the maximum perimeter.

5. To inscribe in a semicircle the maximum rectangle.

6. Find the area of the maximum triangle inscribed in a semicircle whose radius is 3 in.

7. Of all polygons of a given number of sides that can be inscribed in a given circle, that which is regular has the maximum area and the maximum perimeter.

8. Of all polygons of a given number of sides that can be circumscribed about a given circle, that which is regular has the minimum area and the minimum perimeter.

9. In a given line required to find a point such that the sum of its distances from two given points on the same side of the line shall be the minimum.

How does $AP + PB$ compare with $A'B$? and this with $A'X + XB$? and this with $AX + XB$? This is the problem of a ray of light from A to the mirror CD, and reflected to B.

10. To divide a given line into two segments such that the sum of the squares on these segments shall be the minimum.

11. To divide a given line into two segments such that their product shall be the maximum.

421. Recreations of Geometry. The following simple puzzles and recreations of geometry may serve the double purpose of adding interest to the study of the subject and of leading the student to exercise greater care in his demonstrations. They have long been used for this purpose and are among the best known puzzles of geometry.

EXERCISE 74

1. To prove that every triangle is isosceles.

Let ABC be a $\triangle$ that is not isosceles.

Take CP the bisector of $\angle ACB$, and ZP the $\perp$ bisector of AB.

These lines must meet, as at P, for otherwise they would be $\parallel$, which would require CP to be $\perp$ to AB, and this could only happen if $\triangle ABC$ were isosceles, which is not the case by hypothesis.

From P draw $PX \perp$ to BC and $PY \perp$ to CA, and draw PA and PB.

Then since ZP is the $\perp$ bisector of AB, $\therefore PA = PB$.

And since CP is the bisector of $\angle ACB$, $\therefore PX = PY$.

$\therefore$ the rt. $\triangle$ PBX and PAY are congruent, and $BX = AY$.

But the rt. $\triangle$ PXC and PYC are also congruent, and $\therefore XC = YC$.

Adding, we have $BX + XC = AY + YC$, or $BC = AC$.

$\therefore \triangle ABC$ is isosceles even though constructed as not isosceles.

2. To prove that part of an angle equals the whole angle.

Take a square $ABCD$, and draw $MM'P$, the $\perp$ bisector of CD. Then $MM'P$ is also the $\perp$ bisector of AB.

From B draw any line BX equal to AB.

Draw DX and bisect it by the $\perp NP$.

Since DX intersects CD, $\perp$s to these lines cannot be parallel, and must meet as at P.

Draw PA, PD, PC, PX, and PB.

Since MP is the $\perp$ bisector of CD, $PD = PC$. Similarly $PA = PB$, and $PD = PX$.

$\therefore PX = PD = PC$.

But $BX = BC$ by construction, and PB is common to $\triangle$ PBX and PBC.

$\therefore \triangle PBX$ is congruent to $\triangle PBC$, and $\angle XBP = \angle CBP$.

$\therefore$ the whole $\angle XBP$ equals the part, $\angle CBP$.

3. To prove that part of an angle equals the whole angle.

Take a right triangle ABC, and construct upon the hypotenuse BC an equilateral triangle BCD, as shown.

On CD lay off CP equal to CA.

Through X, the mid-point of AB, draw PX to meet CB produced at Q. Draw QA.

Draw the $\perp$ bisectors of QA and QP, as YO and ZO. These must meet at some point O because they are $\perp$ to two intersecting lines.

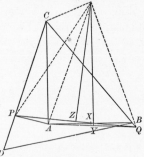

Draw OQ, OA, OP, and OC.

Since O is on the $\perp$ bisector of QA, $\therefore OQ = OA$.

Similarly $OQ = OP$, and $\therefore OA = OP$.

But $CA = CP$, by construction, and $CO = CO$.

$\therefore \triangle AOC$ is congruent to $\triangle POC$, and $\angle ACO = \angle PCO$.

4. To prove that part of a line equals the whole line.

Take a triangle ABC, and draw $CP \perp$ to AB. From C draw CX, making $\angle ACX = \angle B$. Then $\triangle ABC$ and ACX are similar.

$\therefore \triangle ABC : \triangle ACX = \overline{BC}^2 : \overline{CX}^2$.

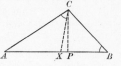

Furthermore $\triangle ABC : \triangle ACX = AB : AX$.

$$\therefore \overline{BC}^2 : \overline{CX}^2 = AB : AX,$$

or $$\overline{BC}^2 : AB = \overline{CX}^2 : AX.$$

But $$\overline{BC}^2 = \overline{AC}^2 + \overline{AB}^2 - 2AB \cdot AP,$$

and $$\overline{CX}^2 = \overline{AC}^2 + \overline{AX}^2 - 2AX \cdot AP.$$

$$\therefore \frac{\overline{AC}^2 + \overline{AB}^2 - 2AB \cdot AP}{AB} = \frac{\overline{AC}^2 + \overline{AX}^2 - 2AX \cdot AP}{AX},$$

or $$\frac{\overline{AC}^2}{AB} + AB - 2AP = \frac{\overline{AC}^2}{AX} + AX - 2AP.$$

$$\therefore \frac{\overline{AC}^2}{AB} - AX = \frac{\overline{AC}^2}{AX} - AB,$$

or $$\frac{\overline{AC}^2 - AB \cdot AX}{AB} = \frac{\overline{AC}^2 - AB \cdot AX}{AX}.$$

$$\therefore AB = AX.$$

5. To show geometrically that $1 = 0$.

Take a square that is 8 units on a side, and cut it into three parts, A, B, C, as shown in the right-hand figure. Fit these parts together as in the left-hand figure.

Now the square is 8 units on a side, and therefore contains 8×8, or 64, small squares, while the rectangle is 13 units long and 5 units high, and therefore contains 5×13, or 65, small squares.

But the two figures are each made up of $A + B + C$ (Ax.11), and therefore are equal (Ax.8).

$\therefore 65 = 64$, and by subtracting 64 we have $1 = 0$ (Ax. 2).

6. To prove that any point on a line bisects it.

Take any point P on AB.

On AB construct an isosceles $\triangle ABC$, having $AC = BC$; and draw PC.

Then in $\triangle APC$ and PBC, we have

$$\angle A = \angle B, \qquad \S\ 74$$
$$AC = BC, \qquad \text{Const.}$$
and $$PC = PC. \qquad \text{Iden.}$$

Three independent parts (that is, not merely the three angles) of one triangle are respectively equal to three parts of the other, and the triangles are congruent; therefore $AP = BP$ (§ 67).

7. To prove that it is possible to let fall two perpendiculars to a line from an external point.

Take two intersecting ⊚ with centers O and O'.

Let one point of intersection be P, and draw the diameters PA and PD.

Draw AD cutting the circumferences at B and C. Then draw PB and PC.

Since $\angle PCA$ is inscribed in a semicircle, it is a right angle. In the same way, since $\angle DBP$ is inscribed in a semicircle, it also is a right angle.

$\therefore PB$ and PC are both $\perp$ to AD.

8. To prove that if two opposite sides of a quadrilateral are equal the figure is an isosceles trapezoid.

Given the quadrilateral $ABCD$, with $BC = DA$.

To prove that AB is $\parallel$ to DC.

Draw MO and NO, the $\perp$ bisectors of AB and CD, to meet at O.

If AB and DC are parallel, the proposition is already proved.

If AB and DC are not parallel, then MO and NO will meet at O, either inside or outside the figure. Let O be supposed to be inside the figure.

Draw OA, OB, OC, OD.

Then since OM is the $\perp$ bisector of AB, $\therefore OA = OB$.

Similarly $OD = OC$.

But DA is given equal to BC.

$\therefore \triangle AOD$ is congruent to $\triangle BOC$,

and $\angle DOA = \angle BOC$.

Also,   rt. $\triangle OCN$ and ODN are congruent,

and $\angle NOD = \angle CON$.

Similarly   rt. $\triangle AMO$ and BMO are congruent,

and $\angle AOM = \angle MOB$.

$\therefore \angle NOD + \angle DOA + \angle AOM = \angle CON + \angle BOC + \angle MOB$,

or $\angle NOM = \angle MON = $ a st. $\angle$.

Therefore the line MON is a straight line, and hence AB is $\parallel$ to DC.

If the point O is outside the quadrilateral, as in the second figure, the proof is substantially the same.

For it can be easily shown that

$$\angle DON - \angle DOA - \angle AOM$$
$$= \angle NOC - \angle BOC - \angle MOB,$$

which is possible only if

$$\angle DON = \angle DOM,$$

or   if ON lies along OM.

But that the proposition is not true is evident from the third figure, in which $BC = DA$, but AB is not $\parallel$ to DC.

422. History of Geometry. The geometry of very ancient peoples was largely the mensuration of simple areas and volumes such as is taught to children in elementary arithmetic to-day. They learned how to find the area of a rectangle, and in the oldest mathematical records that we have there is some discussion of triangles and of the volumes of solids.

The earliest documents that we have, relating to geometry, come to us from Babylon and Egypt. Those from Babylon were written about 2000 B.C. on small clay tablets, some of them about the size of the hand, these tablets afterwards having been baked in the sun. They show that the Babylonians of that period knew something of land measures, and perhaps had advanced far enough to compute the area of a trapezoid. For the mensuration of the circle they later used, as did the early Hebrews, the value $\pi = 3$.

The first definite knowledge that we have of Egyptian mathematics comes to us from a manuscript copied on papyrus, a kind of paper used about the Mediterranean in early times. This copy was made by one Aah-mesu (The Moon-born), commonly called Ahmes, who probably flourished about 1700 B.C. The original from which he copied, written about 2300 B.C., has been lost, but the papyrus of Ahmes, written nearly four thousand years ago, is still preserved and is now in the British Museum. In this manuscript, which is devoted chiefly to fractions and to a crude algebra, is found some work on mensuration. Among the curious rules are the incorrect ones that the area of an isosceles triangle equals half the product of the base and one of the equal sides; and that the area of a trapezoid having bases b, b', and nonparallel sides each equal to a, is $\frac{1}{2} a (b + b')$. One noteworthy advance appears however. Ahmes gives a rule for finding the area of a circle, substantially as follows: Multiply the square on the radius by $(\frac{16}{9})^2$, which is equivalent to taking for π the value 3.1605. Long before the time of Ahmes, however, Egypt had a good working knowledge of practical geometry, as witness the building of the pyramids, the laying out of temples, and the digging of irrigation canals.

From Egypt and possibly from Babylon geometry passed to the shores of Asia Minor and Greece. The scientific study of the subject begins with Thales, one of the Seven Wise Men of the Grecian civilization. Born at Miletus about 640 B.C., he died at Athens in 548 B.C. He spent his early manhood as a merchant, accumulating the wealth that enabled him to spend his later years in study. He visited Egypt and is said to have learned such elements of geometry as were known there. He founded a school of mathematics and philosophy at Miletus, known as the Ionic School. How elementary the knowledge of geometry then was, may be understood from the fact that tradition attributes only about four propositions to Thales, substantially those given in §§ 60, 72, 74, and 215 of this book.

The greatest pupil of Thales, and one of the most remarkable men of antiquity, was Pythagoras. Born probably on the island of Samos, just off the coast of Asia Minor, about the year 580 B.C., Pythagoras set forth as a young man to travel. He went to Miletus and studied under Thales, probably spent several years in study in Egypt, very likely went to Babylon, and possibly went even to India, since tradition asserts this and the nature of his work in mathematics confirms it. In later life he went to southern Italy, and there, at Crotona, in the southeastern part of the peninsula, he founded a school and established a secret society to propagate his doctrines. In geometry he is said to have been the first to demonstrate the proposition that the square on the hypotenuse of a right triangle is equivalent to the sum of the squares on the other two sides (§ 337). The proposition was known before his time, at any rate for special cases, but he seems to have been the first to prove it. To him or to his school seems also to have been due the construction of the regular pentagon (§§ 397, 398) and of the five regular polyhedrons. The construction of the regular pentagon requires the dividing of a line in extreme and mean ratio (§ 311), and this problem is commonly assigned to the Pythagoreans, although it played an important part in Plato's school. Pythagoras is also said to have known that six equilateral triangles, three regular hexagons, or four squares, can be placed about a point so as just to fill the 360°, but that no other regular polygons can be so placed. To his school is also due the proof that the sum of the angles of a triangle equals two right angles (§ 107), and the construction of at least one star-polygon, the star-pentagon, which became the badge of his fraternity.

For two centuries after Pythagoras geometry passed through a period of discovery of propositions. The state of the science may be seen from the fact that Œnopides of Chios, who flourished about 465 B.C., showed how to let fall a perpendicular to a line (§ 227), and how to construct an angle equal to a given angle (§ 232). A few years later, about 440 B.C., Hippocrates of Chios wrote the first Greek textbook on mathematics. He knew that the areas of circles are proportional to the squares on their radii, but was ignorant of the fact that equal central angles or equal inscribed angles intercept equal arcs.

About 430 B.C. Antiphon and Bryson, two Greek teachers, worked on the mensuration of the circle. The former attempted to find the area by doubling the number of sides of a regular inscribed polygon, and the latter by doing the same for both inscribed and circumscribed polygons. They thus substantially exhausted the area between the circle and the polygon, and hence this method was known as the Method of Exhaustions.

During this period the great philosophic school of Plato (429–348 B.C.) flourished at Athens, and to this school is due the first systematic attempt to create exact definitions, axioms, and postulates, and to distinguish between elementary and higher geometry. At this time elementary geometry became limited to the use of the compasses and the unmarked straight edge, which took from this domain the possibility of constructing a square equivalent to a given circle ("squaring the circle"), of trisecting any given angle, and of constructing a cube with twice the volume of a given cube ("duplicating the cube"), these being the three most famous problems of antiquity. Plato and his school were interested in the so-called Pythagorean numbers, numbers that represent the three sides of a right triangle. Pythagoras had already given a rule to the effect that $\frac{1}{4}(m^2+1)^2 = m^2 + \frac{1}{4}(m^2-1)^2$. The school of Plato found that $[(\frac{1}{2}m)^2+1]^2 = m^2 + [(\frac{1}{2}m)^2-1]^2$. By giving various values to m, different numbers will be found such that the sum of the squares of two of them is equal to the square of the third.

The first great textbook on geometry, and the most famous one that has ever appeared, was written by Euclid, who taught mathematics in the great university at Alexandria, Egypt, about 300 B.C. Alexandria was then practically a Greek city, having been named in honor of Alexander the Great, and being ruled by the Greeks.

Euclid's work is known as the "Elements," and, as was the case with all ancient works, the leading divisions were called books, as is seen in the Bible and in such Latin writers as Cæsar and Vergil. This is why we speak of the various books of geometry to-day. In this work Euclid placed all the leading propositions of plane geometry as then known, and arranged them in a logical order. Most subsequent geometries of any importance since his time have been based upon Euclid, improving the sequence, symbols, and wording as occasion demanded.

Euclid did not give much solid geometry because not much was known then. It was to Archimedes (287–212 B.C.), a famous mathematician of Syracuse, on the island of Sicily, that some of the most important propositions of solid geometry are due, particularly those relating to the sphere and cylinder.

He also showed how to find the approximate value of π by a method similar to the one we teach to-day (§ 404), proving that the real value lies between $3\frac{1}{7}$ and $3\frac{10}{71}$. Tradition says that the sphere and cylinder were engraved upon his tomb. The Greeks contributed little more to elementary geometry, although Apollonius of Perga, who taught at Alexandria between 250 and 200 B.C., wrote extensively on conic sections; and Heron of Alexandria, about the beginning of the Christian era, showed that the area of a triangle whose sides are a, b, c, equals $\sqrt{s(s-a)(s-b)(s-c)}$, where $s = \frac{1}{2}(a+b+c)$ (see p. 211).

The East did little for geometry, although contributing considerably to algebra. The first great Hindu writer was Aryabhatta, who was born in 476 A.D. He gave the very close approximation for π, expressed in modern notation as 3.1416. The Arabs, about the time of the Arabian Nights Tales (800 A.D.), did much for mathematics, translating the Greek authors into their own language and also bringing learning from India. Indeed, it is to them that modern Europe owes its first knowledge of Euclid. They contributed nothing of importance to geometry, however.

Euclid was translated from the Arabic into Latin in the twelfth century, Greek manuscripts not being then at hand, or being neglected because of ignorance of the language. The leading translators were Athelhard of Bath (1120), an English monk who had learned Arabic in Spain or in Egypt; Gerhard of Cremona, an Italian monk; and Johannes Campanus, chaplain to Pope Urban IV.

In the Middle Ages in Europe nothing worthy of note was added to the geometry of the Greeks. The first edition of Euclid was printed in Latin in 1482, the first one in English appearing in 1570. Our symbols are modern, $+$ and $-$ first appearing in a German work in 1489; $=$ in Recorde's "Whetstone of Witte" in 1557; $>$ and $<$ in the works of Harriot (1560–1621); and $\times$ in a publication by Oughtred (1574–1660).

423. Notation used in Formulas. Following the general custom, small letters represent numerical values, large letters represent points. The following abbreviations have been used in this book as consistently as the circumstances would allow, the context telling which abbreviation is intended:

a = area, apothem
a, b, c = sides of $\triangle ABC$.
a' = projection of a.
b, b' = bases.
c = circumference.
d = diameter, diagonal.
h = height, altitude.

l = length.
m = median.
p = perimeter.
r = radius.
s = semiperimeter of $\triangle$, $\frac{1}{2}(a + b + c)$.
π = 3.1416, or about $3\frac{1}{7}$.

424. Formulas for Line Values. The following are the most important formulas in line values:

Right triangle, $a^2 + b^2 = c^2$ (§ 337).
Any triangle, $a^2 + b^2 \pm 2\,ab' = c^2$ (§§ 341, 342).
Circle, $c = 2\,\pi r = \pi d$ (§ 385).
Radius of circle, $r = c \div 2\,\pi$.
Equilateral triangle, $h = \frac{1}{2}\,b\,\sqrt{3}$.
Diagonal of square, $d = b\,\sqrt{2}$ (§ 339).
Side of square, $b = \sqrt{a}$.

425. Areas of Plane Figures. The following are the formulas for the areas of the most important plane figures:

Rectangle, bh (§ 320).
Square, b^2 (§ 320).
Parallelogram, bh (§ 322).
Triangle, $\frac{1}{2}bh$ (§ 325), $\sqrt{s(s-a)(s-b)(s-c)}$.
Equilateral triangle, $\frac{1}{4}b^2\sqrt{3}$.
Trapezoid, $\frac{1}{2}h\,(b + b')$ (§ 329).
Regular polygon, $\frac{1}{2}ap$ (§ 386).
Circle, $\frac{1}{2}rc = \pi r^2$ (§§ 388, 389).

INDEX